COLERIDGE'S

POETICAL WORKS

# THE POETICAL AND DRAMATIC WORKS OF SAMUEL TAYLOR COLERIDGE

FOUNDED ON THE AUTHOR'S LATEST EDITION OF 1834 WITH MANY ADDITIONAL PIECES NOW FIRST INCLUDED AND WITH A COLLECTION OF VARIOUS READINGS

IN FOUR VOLUMES

VOLUME TWO

London
MACMILLAN AND CO.
1880

# CONTENTS.

POEMS PUBLISHED IN 1798:—                          PAGE

    France.  An Ode . . . . . . 3
    Frost at Midnight . . . . . 9
    Fears in Solitude . . . . . 12
    The Nightingale : a Conversational Poem . . 21
    The Rime of the Ancient Mariner . . 26

SIBYLLINE LEAVES :—

    Christabel . . . . . . . 61
    Introduction to the Tale of The Dark Ladie . 91
    The Ballad of The Dark Ladie : a Fragment . 97
    Lewti, or the Circassian's Love-Chant . . 100
    The Picture, or The Lover's Resolution . . 104
    Apologetic Preface to "Fire, Famine and Slaughter" 113
    Fire, Famine, and Slaughter.  A War Eclogue . 132
    The Devil's Thoughts . . . . 135
    The Two Round Spaces on the Tombstone . . 141
    Recantation.  Illustrated in the Story of the Mad Ox 143
    Talleyrand to Lord Grenville.  A Metrical Epistle . 149
    A Stranger Minstrel . . . . . 158

EPIGRAMS :—

    To Mr. Pye, on his *Carmen Seculare* . . 161
    "O would the Baptist come again" . . 162
    Occasioned by the former . . . 162
    On a Reader of his Own Verses . . 162
    "If the guilt of all lying consists in deceit" . 163
    "Jack drinks fine wines, wears modish clothing," 163
    "As Dick and I at Charing Cross were walking" 163
    To a Proud Parent . . . . . 164

EPIGRAMS *(continued)* :—

PAGE

"Hippona lets no silly flush" . . . . 164

"Thy lap-dog, Rufa, is a dainty beast" . . 164

"Jem writes his verses with more speed" . . 164

"Doris can find no taste in tea" . . . 165

"What? rise again with *all* one's bones?" . . 165

On a Bad Singer . . . . . . 165

Occasioned by the last . . . . . 165

On a Modern Dramatist . . . . . 165

Directory and Direct-tory . . . . 166

On a very ugly woman . . . . . 166

"There comes from old Avaro's grave" . . 166

"Last Monday all the papers said" . . . 166

To a Critic who quoted an isolated passage, and
    then declared it unintelligible . . . 167

Song to be sung by the lovers of all the noble liquors
    comprised under the name of Ale . . 167

Epitaph on a Bad Man . . . . . 168

Drinking *versus* Thinking ; or, a Song against the
    New Philosophy . . . . . . 168

A Hint to Premiers and First Consuls . . . 169

The Wills of the Wisp : a Sapphic . . . 169

Westphalian Song . . . . . . 170

"What is an Epigram? a dwarfish whole" . 171

"Charles, grave or merry, at no lie would stick" . 171

"An evil spirit 's on thee, friend! of late" . 171

"Here lies the Devil—ask no other name" . 171

To one who published in print what had been
    entrusted to him by my fireside . . . 172

"Scarce any scandal, but has a handle" . 172

"How seldom, friend, a good great man inherits" 172

Reply to the above . . . . . 173

"Old Harpy jeers at castles in the air" . . 173

To a vain young lady . . . . 173

"From me, Aurelia, you desired" . . . 174

For a House-dog's collar . . . . 174

Epigrams *(continued)* :—

    PAGE

    "In vain I praise thee, Zoilus" . . . 174

    Epitaph on a Mercenary Miser . . . 174

    A Dialogue between an Author and his Friend . 175

    Μωροσοφια, or Wisdom in Folly . . . 175

    "Each Bond-street buck conceits, unhappy elf !" . 176

    From an Old German Poet . . . 176

    On the Curious circumstance that in the German
        language the Sun is feminine and the Moon
        masculine . . . . . 176

    Spots in the Sun . . . . . 177

    "When Surface talks of other people's worth" . 177

    To my Candle. The Farewell Epigram . 178

    "An excellent adage commands that we should" 178

Sibylline Leaves :—

    Lines to W. L., Esq., while he sang a song to
        Purcell's music . . . . . 181

    To an Unfortunate Woman at the Theatre . 181

    Lines composed in a Concert-Room . . 183

    The Keepsake . . . . . 186

    The Day-dream. From an Emigrant to his absent
        Wife . . . . . . 188

    To a Young Lady, on her Recovery from a Fever . 189

    Something Childish, but very Natural. Written in
        Germany . . . . . 190

    Homesick. Written in Germany . . . 191

    Answer to a Child's Question . . . 192

    On Revisiting the Sea-shore, after long absence,
        under strong medical reccommendation not to
        bathe . . . . . . 193

    Hymn before Sunrise in the Vale of Chamouni . 194

    The British Stripling's War-Song . . 200

    Lines written in the Album at Elbingerode, in the
        Hartz Forest . . . . . 201

    Inscription for a Fountain on a Heath . . 203

    A Tombless Epitaph . . . . 204

SIBYLLINE LEAVES *(continued)* :— PAGE

This Lime-tree Bower my Prison . . . . 206

Ode to Georgiana, Duchess of Devonshire, on the twenty-fourth Stanza in her " Passage over Mount Gothard " . . . . . . 210

Tranquillity : an Ode . . . . . . 214

Dejection : an Ode . . . . . . 216

To a Friend who had declared his intention of writing no more poetry . . . . . 222

To William Wordsworth. Composed on the night after his recitation of a Poem on the Growth of an Individual Mind . . . . . 224

A Christmas Carol . . . . . . 228

The Virgin's Cradle-Hymn . . . . . 230

Translation of a Passage in Ottfried's Metrical Paraphrase of the Gospel . . . . 231

To Two Sisters : A Wanderer's Farewell . . 233

Farewell to Love . . . . . . 235

The Butterfly . . . . . . . 236

Mutual Passion. Altered and modernized from an old Poet. . . . . . . . 236

The Three Graves. A Fragment of a Sexton's Tale . . . . . . . . 238

The Night-Scene. A Dramatic Fragment . . 254

To a Lady. With Falconer's Shipwreck . . 257

The Visionary Hope . . . . . . 259

The Happy Husband. A Fragment . . . 260

Recollections of Love . . . . . . 261

An Ode to the Rain, composed before daylight on the morning appointed for the departure of a very worthy, but not very pleasant Visitor, whom it was feared the rain might detain . 262

Elegy, imitated from one of Akenside's Blank-verse Inscriptions . . . . . . 265

Separation . . . . . . . 266

Epitaph on an Infant . . . . . . 267

# CONTENTS.

SIBYLLINE LEAVES (*continued*) :—                                    PAGE

Tell's Birthplace.  Imitated from Stolberg .      .    268

Human Life.  On the Denial of Immortality.  A
    Fragment    .    .    .    .    .    .    .    269

Moles    .    .    .    .    .    .    .    .    270

The Visit of the Gods.  Imitated from Schiller  .    270

The Pang more Sharp than All.  An Allegory   .    272

Kubla Khan : or a Vision in a Dream    .    .    274

The Pains of Sleep   .    .    .    .    .    278

Limbo    .    .    .    .    .    .    .    280

Ne Plus Ultra   .    .    .    .    .    .    281

Fragment of a Poem, entitled " The Wanderings
    of Cain "    .    .    .    .    .    .    .    282

Israel's Lament.  Translation of a Hebrew Dirge,
    by Hyman Hurwitz, chanted in the Great
    Synagogue on the day of the Funeral of the
    Princess Charlotte    .    .    .    .    282

Alice Du Clos : or The Forked Tongue.  A Ballad    285

The Knight's Tomb    .    .    .    .    .    292

Hymn to the Earth.  Hexameters    .    .    .    293

Written during a temporary blindness, in the year
    1799    .    .    .    .    .    .    .    .    295

Mahomet    .    .    .    .    .    .    .    296

Catullian Hendecasyllables .    .    .    .    .    297

Duty surviving Self-love, the only sure friend of
    declining life.  A Soliloquy    .    .    .    298

Phantom or Fact ?  A Dialogue in Verse    .    .    298

Phantom    .    .    .    .    .    .    .    299

Work without Hope    .    .    .    .    .    300

Youth and Age    .    .    .    .    .    .    300

A Day-Dream    .    .    .    .    .    .    303

First Advent of Love .    .    .    .    .    .    304

Names    .    .    .    .    .    .    .    305

Water Ballad    .    .    .    .    .    .    305

Desire    .    .    .    .    .    .    .    306

Love and Frendship Opposite    .    .    .    .    307

## CONTENTS.

SIBYLLINE LEAVES (*continued*) :—                                   PAGE

Not at Home . . . . . . . . 307

To a Lady offended by a sportive observation that
    women have no souls . . . . . 308

"I have heard of reasons manifold" . . . 308

Lines suggested by the last words of Berengarius . 308

*Sancti Dominici Pallium ;* a Dialogue between Poet
    and Friend . . . . . . . 310

Lines to a Comic Author, on an abusive Review . 313

Constancy to an Ideal Object . . . . 313

Modern Critics . . . . . . . 315

"The poet in his lone yet genial hour" . . 315

Inscription for a Time-piece . . . . 316

Fancy in Nubibus : or the Poet in the Clouds. A
    Sonnet composed on the Sea-Coast . . 316

The Blossoming of the Solitary Date Tree . . 317

The Exchange . . . . . . . 320

Love's Burial-Place . . . . . . 321

The Suicide's Argument . . . . . 321

    Nature's Answer . . . . . 321

The Two Founts . . . . . . . 322

"Yes, yes ! that boon, life's richest treat" . . 324

The Garden of Boccaccio . . . . . 326

On a Cataract from a cavern near the summit of a
    mountain precipice . . . . . 331

A Child's Evening Prayer . . . . . 332

Love's Apparition and Evanishment. An Allegoric
    Romance . . . . . . . 332

    L'Envoy . . . . . . . 333

Love, Hope, and Patience in Education . . 334

A Character . . . . . . . 335

The Reproof and Reply . . . . . 338

Cholera cured beforehand . . . . . 340

Cologne . . . . . . . . 342

On my joyful departure from the same city . . 342

# CONTENTS.

SIBYLLINE LEAVES (*continued*) :—                    PAGE

Written in an Album . . . . . 343
Metrical Feet. Lesson for a Boy . . . 343
The Homeric Hexameter and the Ovidian Elegiac
　　Metre described and exemplified . . 344
To the Young Artist, Kayser of Kaserwerth. . 345
Job's Luck . . . . . . . 345
On an Insignificant . . . . . 346
Profuse Kindness . . . . . 346
Charity in Thought . . . . . 346
A Thought suggested by a View of Saddleback
　　in Cumberland . . . . . 347
Song, *ex improviso*, on hearing a song in praise of
　　a Lady's Beauty . . . . . 347
"In many ways doth the full heart reveal" . 347
What is Life? . . . . . . 348
Humility the Mother of Charity . . . 348
On an Infant which died before Baptism . 348
*E cœlo descendit* γνῶθι σεαυτόν . . . 349
"Beareth all things" . . . . . 349
My Baptismal Birth-day . . . . 350
Epitaphium Testamentarium . . . 351
Epitaph . . . . . . . 351

SUPPLEMENT :—

Monody on the Death of Chatterton . . 355*
To the Evening Star . . . . . 359*
Anna and Harland . . . . . 359*
Translation of Wrangham's *Hendecasyllabi ad*
　　*Bruntonam e Granta Exituram* . . 360*
To Miss Brunton, with the preceding translation . 362*
The Mad Monk . . . . . . 362*

APPENDIX :—

The Old Man of the Alps . . . . 355
Poems and Poetical Fragments . . . 359

APPENDIX (*continued*) :—                                    PAGE

   Translation of a Latin Inscription by the Rev. W.
     L. Bowles, in Nether Stowey Church .    . 365

   Epilogue to the Rash Conjurer    .    .    .    . 366

   Sentimental    .    .    .    .    .    .    . 366

   The Alternative .    .    .    .    .    .    . 366

   Written on the fly-leaf of a copy of " Field on the
     Church"    .    .    .    .    .    .    . 367

   Translation of a Fragment of Heraclitus    .    . 367

   Epigrams .    .    .    .    .    .    .    . 368

   Sonnet on receiving a letter informing me of the
     birth of a son    .    .    .    .    .    . 369

   On Deputy    .    .    .    .    .    .    . 369

   To a well-known Musical Critic .    .    .    . 370

   Εγωενκαιπαν    .    .    .    .    .    .    . 370

   The Bridge-Street Committee—An Impromptu .  371

   To Nature .    .    .    .    .    .    .    . 372

   " What boots to tell how o'er his grave"    .    . 373

   Mr. Baker's courtship    .    .    .    .    . 373

   Lines in a German Student's Album    .    .    . 373

   On Kepler .    .    .    .    .    .    .    . 374

   Distich from the Greek    .    .    .    .    . 374

NOTES    .    .    .    .    .    .    .    .    . 375

# POEMS

### PUBLISHED IN 1798.

[The first division of this section includes three poems—*Fears in Solitude, France, an Ode,* and *Frost at Midnight,* published by Coleridge in a separate quarto pamphlet in the year 1798. The second division contains *The Nightingale* and the most famous of all Coleridge's poems, *The Ancient Mariner,* both contributed to *Lyrical Ballads* in the same year.]

# FRANCE.  AN ODE.*

## ARGUMENT.

*First Stanza.* An invocation to those objects in Nature the contemplation of which had inspired the Poet with a devotional love of Liberty. *Second Stanza.* The exultation of the Poet at the commencement of the French Revolution, and his unqualified abhorrence of the Alliance against the Republic. *Third Stanza.* The blasphemies and horrors during the domination of the Terrorists regarded by the Poet as a transient storm, and as the natural consequence of the former despotism and of the foul superstition of Popery. Reason, indeed, began to suggest many apprehensions; yet still the Poet struggled to retain the hope that France would make conquests by no other means than by presenting to the observation of Europe a people more happy and better instructed than under other forms of Government. *Fourth Stanza.* Switzerland, and the Poet's recantation. *Fifth Stanza.* An address to Liberty, in which the Poet expresses his conviction that those feelings and that grand *ideal* of Freedom which the mind attains by its contemplation of its individual nature, and of the sublime surrounding objects (see stanza the first) do not belong to men as a society, nor can possibly be either gratified or realized under any form of human government; but belong to the individual man, so far as he is pure, and inflamed with the love and adoration of God in Nature.

* First printed in *The Morning Post* of April 16, 1798, under the title of *The Recantation : an Ode*, and afterwards, with its

### I.

YE Clouds ! that far above me float and pause,
   Whose pathless march no mortal may control !*
Ye Ocean-Waves ! that, wheresoe'er ye roll,
Yield homage only to eternal laws !
Ye Woods ! that listen to the night-bird's singing,
   Midway the smooth and perilous slope† reclined,
Save when your own imperious branches swinging,
   Have made a solemn music of the wind !
Where, like a man beloved of God,
Through glooms, which never woodman trod,
   How oft, pursuing fancies holy,
My moonlight way o'er flowering weeds I wound,
Inspired, beyond the guess of folly,
By each rude shape and wild unconquerable sound !
O ye loud Waves ! and O ye Forests high !
   And O ye Clouds that far above me soar'd !
Thou rising Sun ! thou blue rejoicing sky !
   Yea, everything that is and will be free !
   Bear witness for me, wheresoe'er ye be,
With what deep worship I have still adored
   The spirit of divinest Liberty.

### II.

When France in wrath her giant limbs uprear'd,
   And with that oath, which ‡smote air, earth, and
     sea,

---

present title, in the same quarto pamphlet with *Fears in Solitude*. Reprinted in *The Morning Post*, Oct. 14, 1802, with the addition of an Argument.

  * Veering your pathless march without control.—1802.

  † Steep.—1798.      ‡ Shook.—1802.

Stamp'd her strong foot and said she would be
    free,
Bear witness for me, how I hoped and fear'd !
With what a joy my lofty gratulation*
    Unawed I sang, amid a slavish band :
And when to whelm the disenchanted nation,
    Like fiends embattled by a wizard's wand,
        The Monarchs march'd † in evil day,
        And Britain join'd the dire array ;
    Though dear her shores and circling ocean,
Though many friendships, many youthful loves
    Had swoln the patriot emotion
And flung ‡ a magic light o'er all her hills and
    groves ;
Yet still my voice, unalter'd, sang defeat
    To all that braved the tyrant-quelling lance,
And shame too long delay'd and vain retreat !
For ne'er, O Liberty ! with partial aim
I dimm'd thy light or damp'd thy holy flame ;
But bless'd the pæans of deliver'd France,
And hung my head and wept at Britain's name.

### III.

" And what," I said, " though Blasphemy's loud
    scream
    With that sweet music§ of deliverance strove !
    Though all the fierce and drunken passions wove
A dance more wild than e'er was maniac's dream !

---

* Eager gratulation.—1802.        † Moved.—*Ib.*
‡ Spread.—*Ib.*        § Those sweet pæans.—*Ib.*

Ye storms, that round the dawning east assembled,
The Sun was rising, though ye hid his light!"
    And when, to soothe my soul, that hoped and
        trembled,       [bright;
    The dissonance ceased, and all seem'd calm and
    When France her front deep-scarr'd and gory
    Conceal'd with clustering wreaths of glory
      When, insupportably* advancing,
    Her arm made mockery of the warrior's ramp;
      While timid looks of fury glancing,
    Domestic treason, crush'd beneath her fatal
      stamp,
    Writhed like a wounded dragon in his gore;
    Then I reproach'd† my fears that would not flee;
"And soon," I said, "shall Wisdom teach her lore
In the low huts of them that toil and groan!
And, conquering by her happiness alone,
    Shall France compel‡ the nations to be free,
Till Love and Joy look round, and call the Earth
    their own."

IV.

Forgive me, Freedom! O forgive those dreams!
    I hear thy voice, I hear thy loud lament,
    From bleak Helvetia's icy caverns sent—
I hear thy groans upon her blood-stain'd streams!
    Heroes, that for your peaceful country perish'd,
And ye that, fleeing, spot your mountain-snows
    With bleeding wounds; forgive me, that I che-
    rish'd

---

* Irresistibly.—1802.    † Rebuked.—*1b.*    ‡ Persuade.—*1b.*

One thought that ever bless'd your cruel foes !
   To scatter rage and traitorous guilt
   Where Peace her jealous home had built ;
    A patriot-race to disinherit
Of all that made their stormy wilds* so dear ;
    And with inexpiable spirit
To taint the bloodless freedom of the mountaineer—
O France, that mockest Heaven, adulterous, blind,
   And patriot only in pernicious toils,
Are these thy boasts, Champion of human kind ?
   To mix with Kings in the low lust of sway,
   Yell in the hunt, and share the murderous prey ;
   To insult the shrine of Liberty with spoils
From freemen torn ; to tempt and to betray ? †

v.

   The sensual and the dark rebel in vain,
   Slaves by their own compulsion ! In mad game

* Native wilds.—1802.

† After the fourth Stanza the original version in *The Morning Post* thus continues :—

v.

[The Fifth Stanza, which alluded to the African Slave-trade, as conducted by this country, and to the present Ministry and their supporters, has been omitted ; and would have been omitted without any remark, if the commencing lines of the Sixth Stanza had not referred to it.]

vi.

   Shall I with *these* my patriot zeal combine ?
    No, Afric, no ! They stand before my ken,
    Loathed as th' Hyænas, that in murky den
   Whine o'er their prey, and mangle while they whine !
   Divinest Liberty ! with vain endeavour, &c.
                    1798.

They burst their manacles and wear the name
  Of Freedom, graven on a heavier chain !
O Liberty ! with profitless endeavour
Have I pursued thee, many a weary hour ;
  But thou nor swell'st the victor's strain, nor ever
Didst breathe thy soul in forms of human power.
  Alike from all, howe'er they praise thee,
  (Nor prayer, nor boastful name delays thee)
    Alike from Priestcraft's* harpy minions,
  And factious Blasphemy's obscener slaves,
    Thou speedest on thy subtle pinions,
The guide of homeless winds, and playmate of the
      waves ! †
And there I felt thee !—on that sea-cliff's verge,
  Whose pines, scarce travell'd by the breeze
      above,
Had made one murmur with the distant surge !
Yes, while I stood and gazed, my temples bare,
And shot my being through earth, sea and air,
  Possessing all things with intensest love,
    O Liberty ! my spirit felt thee there.

  *February*, 1798.

---

* Priesthood's.—1798.

† To live amid the winds, and move upon the waves.—*Ib.*

‡ To live among the winds, and brood upon the waves.—1802.

## FROST AT MIDNIGHT.*

THE frost performs its secret ministry,
  Unhelp'd by any wind. The owlet's cry
Came loud—and hark, again ! loud as before.
The inmates of my cottage, all at rest,
Have left me to that solitude which suits
Abstruser musings : save that at my side
My cradled infant slumbers peacefully.
'Tis calm indeed ! so calm, that it disturbs
And vexes meditation with its strange
And extreme silentness. Sea, hill, and wood,
This populous village ! sea, and hill, and wood,
With all the numberless goings-on of life,
Inaudible as dreams ! The thin blue flame
Lies on my low-burnt fire, and quivers not ;
Only that film,† which flutter'd on the grate,
Still flutters there, the sole unquiet thing.
Methinks, its motion in this hush of nature
Gives it dim sympathies with me who live,
Making it a companionable form,
Whose puny flaps and freaks the idling Spirit
By its own moods interprets, every where
Echo or mirror seeking of itself,
And makes a toy of Thought.

* Printed in 1798 at the end of the quarto pamphlet also
containing *Fears in Solitude*, and *France, an Ode*.

† In all parts of the kingdom these films are called
*strangers*, and supposed to portend the arrival of some absent
friend. (Note by S. T. C. in 1798.)

But O ! how oft,
How oft, at school, with most believing mind,
Presageful, have I gazed upon the bars,
To watch that fluttering stranger ! and as oft *
With unclosed lids, already had I dreamt
Of my sweet birth-place, and the old church-tower,
Whose bells, the poor man's only music, rang
From morn to evening, all the hot Fair-day,
So sweetly, that they stirr'd and haunted me
With a wild pleasure, falling on mine ear
Most like articulate sounds of things to come !
So gazed I, till the soothing things I dreamt
Lull'd me to sleep, and sleep prolong'd my dreams !
And so I brooded all the following morn,
Awed by the stern preceptor's face, mine eye
Fix'd with mock study on my swimming book :
Save if the door half open'd, and I snatch'd
A hasty glance, and still my heart leapt up,

* Making it a companionable form
    With which I can hold commune.  Idle thought !
    But still the living spirit in our frame,
    That loves not to behold a lifeless thing,
    Transfuses into all its own delights,
    Its own volition, sometimes with deep faith,
    And sometimes with fantastic playfulness.
    Ah me ! amused by no such curious toys
    Of the self-watching subtilizing mind,
    How often in my early school-boy days,
    With most believing superstitious wish
    Presageful have I gazed upon the bars,
    To watch the *stranger* there ! and oft belike, &c.

1798.

For still I hoped to see the stranger's face,
Townsman, or aunt, or sister more beloved,
My play-mate when we both were clothed alike !

Dear babe, that sleepest cradled by my side,
Whose gentle breathings, heard in this deep calm,*
Fill up the interspersed vacancies
And momentary pauses of the thought !
My babe so beautiful ! it thrills† my heart
With tender gladness, thus to look at thee,
And think that thou shalt learn far other lore,
And in far other scenes !   For I was rear'd
In the great city, pent 'mid cloisters dim,
And saw nought lovely but the sky and stars.
But thou, my babe ! shalt wander like a breeze
By lakes and sandy shores, beneath the crags
Of ancient mountain, and beneath the clouds,
Which image in their bulk both lakes and shores
And mountain crags : so shalt thou see and hear
The lovely shapes and sounds intelligible
Of that eternal language, which thy God
Utters, who from eternity doth teach
Himself in all, and all things in himself.
Great universal Teacher ! he shall mould
Thy spirit, and by giving make it ask.

Therefore all seasons shall be sweet to thee,
Whether the summer clothe the general earth
With greenness, or the redbreast sit and sing

---

\* Dead calm.—1798—1817.        † Fills.—*ib.*

Betwixt the tufts of snow on the bare branch
Of mossy apple-tree, while the nigh thatch*
Smokes in the sun-thaw; whether the eave-drops
    fall
Heard only in the trances of the blast,
Or if the secret ministry of frost †
Shall hang them up in silent icicles,
Quietly shining to the quiet Moon.
[Like those, my babe! which ere to-morrow's
    warmth
Have capp'd their sharp keen points with pendu-
    lous drops,
Will catch thine eye, and with their novelty
Suspend thy little soul; then make thee shout,
And stretch and flutter from thy mother's arms
As thou would'st fly for very eagerness.]

> *February,* 1798.


## FEARS IN SOLITUDE.

### WRITTEN IN APRIL, 1798, DURING THE ALARM OF AN INVASION.

A GREEN and silent spot amid the hills,
    A small and silent dell! O'er stiller place
No singing sky-lark ever poised himself.
The hills are heathy, save that swelling slope,

* While all the thatch.—1798.
† Or whether the secret ministry of cold.—*Ib.*

Which hath a gay and gorgeous covering on,
All golden with the never-bloomless furze,
Which now blooms most profusely : but the dell,
Bathed by the mist, is fresh and delicate
As vernal corn-field, or the unripe flax,
When through its half-transparent stalks, at eve,
The level sunshine glimmers with green light.
Oh ! 'tis a quiet spirit-healing nook !
Which all, methinks, would love ; but chiefly he,
The humble man, who, in his youthful years,
Knew just so much of folly, as had made
His early manhood more securely wise !
Here he might lie on fern or wither'd heath,
While from the singing lark (that sings unseen
The minstrelsy that solitude loves best),
And from the sun, and from the breezy air,
Sweet influences trembled o'er his frame ;
And he, with many feelings, many thoughts,
Made up a meditative joy, and found
Religious meanings in the forms of Nature !
And so, his senses gradually wrapt
In a half sleep, he dreams of better worlds,
And dreaming hears thee still, O singing lark ;
That singest like an angel in the clouds !

My God ! it is a melancholy thing
For such a man, who would full fain preserve
His soul in calmness, yet perforce must feel
For all his human brethren—O my God !
It [is indeed a melancholy thing,
And] weighs upon the heart, that he must think

What uproar and what strife may now be stirring
This way or that way o'er these silent hills—
Invasion, and the thunder and the shout,
And all the crash of onset ; fear and rage,
And undetermined conflict—even now,
Even now, perchance, and in his native isle :
Carnage and groans* beneath this blessed sun !
We have offended, O, my countrymen !
We have offended very grievously,
And been most tyrannous.† From east to west
A groan of accusation pierces Heaven !
The wretched plead against us ; multitudes
Countless and vehement, the sons of God,
Our brethren ! Like a cloud that travels on,
Steam'd up from Cairo's swamps of pestilence,
Even so, my countrymen ! have we gone forth
And borne to distant tribes slavery and pangs,
And, deadlier far, our vices, whose deep taint
With slow perdition murders the whole man,
His body and his soul ! Meanwhile, at home,
All individual dignity and power
Engulf'd in courts, committees, institutions,
Associations and societies,
A vain, speech-mouthing, speech-reporting guild,
One benefit-club for mutual flattery,‡
We have drunk up, demure as at a grace,§

---

* Carnage and screams.—1798.

† And have been tyrannous.—*Ib.*

‡ The above five lines are not in the original quarto.—Ed.

§ We have been drinking with a riotous thirst.—1798.

Pollutions from the brimming cup of wealth ;
[A selfish, lewd, effeminated race,]
Contemptuous of all honourable rule,
Yet bartering freedom and the poor man's life
For gold, as at a market ! The sweet words
Of Christian promise, words that even yet
Might stem destruction, were they wisely preach'd,
Are mutter'd o'er by men, whose tones proclaim
How flat and wearisome they feel their trade :
Rank scoffers some, but most too indolent
To deem them falsehoods or to know their truth.
Oh ! blasphemous ! the book of life is made
A superstitious instrument, on which
We gabble o'er the oaths we mean to break ;
For all must swear—all and in every place,
College and wharf, council and justice-court ;
All, all must swear, the briber and the bribed,
Merchant and lawyer, senator and priest,
The rich, the poor, the old man and the young ;
All, all make up one scheme of perjury,
That faith doth reel ; the very name of God
Sounds like a juggler's charm ; and, bold with joy,
Forth from his dark and lonely hiding-place,
(Portentous sight !) the owlet Atheism,
Sailing on obscene wings athwart the noon,
Drops his blue-fringed lids, and holds them close,
And hooting at the glorious sun in Heaven,
Cries out, " Where is it ?"

                    Thankless too for peace,
(Peace long preserved by fleets and perilous seas)

Secure from actual warfare, we have loved
To swell the war-whoop, passionate for war!
Alas! for ages ignorant of all
Its ghastlier workings, (famine or blue plague,
Battle, or siege, or flight through wintry snows,)
We, this whole people, have been clamorous
For war and bloodshed; animating sports,
The which we pay for as a thing to talk of,
Spectators and not combatants! No guess
Anticipative of a wrong unfelt,
No speculation on contingency,
However dim and vague, too vague and dim
To yield a justifying cause; and forth,
(Stuff'd out with big preamble, holy names,
And adjurations of the God in Heaven,)
We send our mandates for the certain death
Of thousands and ten thousands! Boys and girls,
And women, that would groan to see a child
Pull off an insect's leg, all read of war,
The best amusement for our morning meal!
The poor wretch, who has learnt his only prayers
From curses, who knows scarcely words enough
To ask a blessing from his Heavenly Father,
Becomes a fluent phraseman, absolute
And technical in victories and defeats,
And all our dainty terms for fratricide;
Terms which we trundle smoothly o'er our tongues
Like mere abstractions, empty sounds to which
We join no feeling and attach no form!
As if the soldier died without a wound;
As if the fibres of this godlike frame

Were gored without a pang ; as if the wretch,
Who fell in battle, doing bloody deeds,
Pass'd off to Heaven, translated and not kill'd ;
As though he had no wife to pine for him,
No God to judge him !—Therefore, evil days
Are coming on us, O my countrymen !
And what if all-avenging Providence,
Strong and retributive, should make us know
The meaning of our words, force us to feel
The desolation and the agony
Of our fierce doings ?—

      Spare us yet awhile,
Father and God ! O spare us yet awhile !
O let not English women drag their flight
Fainting beneath the burthen of their babes,
Of the sweet infants, that but yesterday
Laugh'd at the breast ! Sons, brothers, husbands, all
Who ever gazed with fondness on the forms
Which grew up with you round the same fire-side,
And all who ever heard the sabbath-bells
Without the infidel's scorn, make yourselves pure !
Stand forth ! be men ! repel an impious foe,
Impious and false, a light yet cruel race,
Who laugh away all virtue, mingling mirth
With deeds of murder ; and still promising
Freedom, themselves too sensual to be free,
Poison life's amities, and cheat the heart
Of faith and quiet hope, and all that soothes
And all that lifts the spirit ! Stand we forth ;
Render them back upon the insulted ocean,

And let them toss as idly on its waves
As the vile sea-weed, which some mountain-blast
Swept from our shores! And oh! may we return
Not with a drunken triumph, but with fear,
Repenting of the wrongs with which we stung
So fierce a foe to frenzy!

                I have told,
O Britons! O my brethren! I have told
Most bitter truth, but without bitterness.
Nor deem my zeal or factious or mis-timed;
For never can true courage dwell with them,
Who, playing tricks with conscience, dare not look
At their own vices.   We have been too long
Dupes of a deep delusion! Some, belike,
Groaning with restless enmity, expect
All change from change of constituted power;
As if a Government had been a robe,
On which our vice and wretchedness were tagg'd
Like fancy-points and fringes, with the robe
Pull'd off at pleasure.   Fondly these attach
A radical causation to a few
Poor drudges of chastising Providence,
Who borrow all their hues and qualities
From our own folly and rank wickedness,
Which gave them birth and nurse them.   Others, meanwhile,
Dote with a mad idolatry; and all
Who will not fall before their images,
And yield them worship, they are enemies
Even of their country!

                              Such have I been deem'd.—
But, O dear Britain! O my mother Isle!
Needs must thou prove a name most dear and holy
To me, a son, a brother, and a friend,
A husband, and a father! who revere
All bonds of natural love, and find them all
Within the limits of thy rocky shores.
O native Britain! O my mother Isle!
How shouldst thou prove aught else but dear and
          holy
To me, who from thy lakes and mountain-hills,
Thy clouds, thy quiet dales, thy rocks and seas,
Have drunk in all my intellectual life,
All sweet sensations, all ennobling thoughts,
All adoration of the God in Nature,
All lovely and all honourable things,
Whatever makes this mortal spirit feel
The joy and greatness of its future being?
There lives nor form nor feeling in my soul
Unborrow'd from my country! O divine
And beauteous island! thou hast been my sole
And most magnificent temple, in the which
I walk with awe, and sing my stately songs,
Loving the God that made me!—

                              May my fears,
My filial fears, be vain! and may the vaunts
And menace of the vengeful enemy
Pass like the gust, that roar'd and died away
In the distant tree: which heard, and only heard
In this low dell, bow'd not the delicate grass.

But now the gentle dew-fall sends abroad
The fruit-like perfume of the golden furze :
The light has left the summit of the hill,
Though still a sunny gleam lies beautiful,
Aslant the ivied beacon.* Now farewell,
Farewell, awhile, O soft and silent spot !
On the green sheep-track, up the heathy hill,
Homeward I wind my way ; and lo ! recall'd
From bodings that have well-nigh wearied me,
I find myself upon the brow, and pause
Startled ! And after lonely sojourning
In such a quiet and surrounded nook,†
This burst of prospect, here the shadowy main,
Dim-tinted, there the mighty majesty
Of that huge amphitheatre of rich
And elmy fields, seems like society—
Conversing with the mind, and giving it
A livelier impulse and a dance of thought ;
And now, beloved Stowey ! I behold
Thy church-tower, and, methinks, the four huge
    elms
Clustering, which mark the mansion of my friend ;
And close behind them, hidden from my view,
Is my own lowly cottage, where my babe
And my babe's mother dwell in peace ! With light
And quicken'd footsteps thitherward I tend,
Remembering thee, O green and silent dell !
And grateful, that by Nature's quietness

* On the long-ivied beacon.—1798.
† Scene.—*Ib.*

And solitary musings, all my heart
Is soften'd, and made worthy to indulge
Love, and the thoughts that yearn for human kind.

*Nether Stowey, April 20th,* 1798.


## THE NIGHTINGALE :

A CONVERSATIONAL POEM, WRITTEN IN APRIL, 1798.*

NO cloud, no relique of the sunken day
        Distinguishes the West, no long thin slip
Of sullen light, no obscure trembling hues.
Come, we will rest on this old mossy bridge !
You see the glimmer of the stream beneath,
But hear no murmuring : it flows silently,
O'er its soft bed of verdure.   All is still,
A balmy night ! and though the stars be dim,
Yet let us think upon the vernal showers
That gladden the green earth, and we shall find
A pleasure in the dimness of the stars.
And hark ! the Nightingale begins its song,
" Most musical, most melancholy " † bird !

---

* First printed in *Lyrical Ballads,* 1798.

† " *Most musical, most melancholy.*" This passage in
Milton possesses an excellence far superior to that of mere
description : it is spoken in the character of the melancholy
man, and has therefore a *dramatic* propriety. The author
makes this remark to rescue himself from the charge of having
alluded with levity to a line in Milton, a charge than which
none could be more painful to him, except perhaps that of
having ridiculed his Bible.

A melancholy bird ?   Oh ! idle thought !
In Nature there is nothing melancholy.
But some night-wandering man whose heart was
    pierced
With the remembrance of a grievous wrong,
Or slow distemper, or neglected love,
(And so, poor wretch ! fill'd all things with himself,
And made all gentle sounds tell back the tale
Of his own sorrow) he, and such as he,
First named these notes a melancholy strain.
And many a poet echoes the conceit ;
Poet who hath been building up the rhyme
When he had better far have stretch'd his limbs
Beside a brook in mossy forest-dell,
By sun or moon-light, to the influxes
Of shapes and sounds and shifting elements
Surrendering his whole spirit, of his song
And of his fame forgetful ! so his fame
Should share in Nature's immortality,
A venerable thing ! and so his song
Should make all Nature lovelier, and itself
Be loved like Nature !   But 'twill not be so ;
And youths and maidens most poetical,
Who lose the deepening twilights of the spring
In ball-rooms and hot theatres, they still
Full of meek sympathy must heave their sighs
O'er Philomela's pity-pleading strains.

   My Friend, and thou, our Sister ! * we have
    learnt

* My Friend and my Friend's Sister.—1798.

A different lore : we may not thus profane
Nature's sweet voices, always full of love
And joyance ! 'Tis the merry Nightingale
That crowds, and hurries, and precipitates
With fast thick warble his delicious notes,
As he were fearful that an April night
Would be too short for him to utter forth
His love-chant, and disburthen his full soul
Of all its music !

     And I know a grove
Of large extent, hard by a castle huge,
Which the great lord inhabits not ; and so
This grove is wild with tangling underwood,
And the trim walks are broken up, and grass,
Thin grass and king-cups grow within the paths.
But never elsewhere in one place I knew
So many nightingales ; and far and near,
In wood and thicket, over the wide grove,
They answer and provoke each other's songs,
With skirmish and capricious passagings,
And murmurs musical and swift jug jug,
And one low piping sound more sweet than all—
Stirring the air with such an harmony,
That should you close your eyes, you might almost
Forget it was not day ! On moonlight bushes,
Whose dewy leafits are but half-disclosed,
You may perchance behold them on the twigs,
Their bright, bright eyes, their eyes both bright and
   full,
Glistening, while many a glow-worm in the shade
Lights up her love-torch.

　　　　　　　　　　A most gentle Maid,
Who dwelleth in her hospitable home
Hard by the castle, and at latest eve
(Even like a Lady vow'd and dedicate
To something more than Nature in the grove)
Glides through the pathways; she knows all their
　　　　notes,
That gentle Maid! and oft, a moment's space,
What time the moon was lost behind a cloud,
Hath heard a pause of silence; till the moon
Emerging, hath awaken'd earth and sky
With one sensation, and those wakeful birds
Have all burst forth in choral minstrelsy,
As if some sudden gale had swept at once
A hundred airy harps!* 　And she hath watch'd
Many a nightingale perch giddily
On blosmy twig still swinging from the breeze,
And to that motion tune his wanton song
Like tipsy joy that reels with tossing head.

　　Farewell, O Warbler! till to-morrow eve,
And you, my friends! farewell, a short farewell!
We have been loitering long and pleasantly,
And now for our dear homes.—That strain again!
Full fain it would delay me! My dear babe,
Who, capable of no articulate sound,
Mars all things with his imitative lisp,
How he would place his hand beside his ear,

　　　* As if one quick and sudden gale had swept
　　　　　An hundred airy harps! 　　　1798-1817.

His little hand, the small forefinger up,
And bid us listen !  And I deem it wise
To make him Nature's playmate.  He knows well
The evening star ; and once, when he awoke
In most distressful mood (some inward pain
Had made up that strange thing, an infant's dream),
I hurried with him to our orchard-plot,
And he beheld * the moon, and, hush'd at once,
Suspends his sobs, and laughs most silently,
While his fair eyes, that swam with undropp'd tears,
Did glitter in the yellow moon-beam !  Well !—
It is a father's tale : But if that Heaven
Should give me life, his childhood shall grow up
Familiar with these songs, that with the night
He may associate joy.—Once more, farewell,
Sweet Nightingale ! once more, my friends ! fare-
    well.

* Beholds.—1798.

# THE RIME OF THE ANCIENT MARINER.*

### IN SEVEN PARTS.†

#### ARGUMENT.

How a Ship having passed the Line was
driven by storms to the cold Country towards
the South Pole; and how from thence she made
her course to the tropical Latitude of the Great
Pacific Ocean; and of the strange things that
befell; and in what manner the Ancient Mariner
came back to his own Country.

## PART I.

An ancient
Mariner
meeteth three
gallants bid-
den to a wed-
ding-feast,
and detaineth
one.

IT is an ancient Mariner,
 And he stoppeth one of three.
" By thy long grey beard and glittering eye,
Now wherefore stopp'st thou me ?‡

---

* *Ancyent Marinere*, in the title and throughout the
text, 1798.  In the edition of 1800, *The Ancient Mariner,
a Poet's Reverie.*

† First printed in *Lyrical Ballads*, Bristol, 1798, and
again in the enlarged London editions of 1800, 1802,
and 1805.

‡ " By thy long grey beard and thy glittering eye
 Now wherefore stoppest me ?"—1798.

"The Bridegroom's doors are open'd wide,
And I am next of kin ;
The guests are met, the feast is set :
May'st hear the merry din."

He holds him with his skinny hand,
'There was a ship," quoth he.
'Hold off ! unhand me, grey-beard loon !"
Eftsoons his hand dropt he.*

He holds him with his glittering eye—
The wedding-guest stood still,
And listens like a three years' child :
The Mariner hath his will.

The wedding-guest sat on a stone :
He cannot choose but hear ;
And thus spake on that ancient man,
The bright-eyed Mariner.

The ship was cheer'd, the harbour clear'd,
Merrily did we drop

The wedding
guest is spell-
bound by the
eye of the old
sea-faring
man, and
constrained
to hear his
tale.

* But still he holds the wedding-guest—
    "There was a Ship," quoth he
  "Nay, if thou'st got a laughsome tale,
    Mariner ! come with me."

  He holds him with his skinny hand,
    Quoth he, "There was a Ship—"
  "Now get thee hence, thou grey-beard Loon !
    Or my staff shall make thee skip."—1798.

Below the kirk, below the hill,
Below the light-house top.

The Mariner
tells how the
ship sailed
southward
with a good
wind and fair
weather, till
it reached the
line.

" The sun came up upon the left,
Out of the sea came he !
And he shone bright, and on the right
Went down into the sea.

" Higher and higher every day,
Till over the mast at noon—"
The Wedding-Guest here beat his breast,
For he heard the loud bassoon.

The wedding
guest heareth
the bridal
music ; but
the mariner
continueth
his tale.

The bride hath paced into the hall,
Red as a rose is she ;
Nodding their heads before her goes
The merry minstrelsy.

— The Wedding-Guest he beat his breast,
Yet he cannot choose but hear ;
And thus spake on that ancient man,
The bright-eyed Mariner.

The ship
drawn by a
storm toward
the south
pole.

\* " And now the storm-blast came, and he
Was tyrannous and strong :

\* Listen, Stranger ! Storm and Wind,
    A Wind and Tempest strong !
For days and weeks it play'd us freaks—
    Like chaff we drove along.

Listen, Stranger ! Mist and Snow,
    And it grew wondrous cauld : &c.—1798.

He struck with his o'ertaking wings,
And chased us south along.

With sloping masts and dipping prow,
As who pursued with yell and blow
Still treads the shadow of his foe,
And forward bends his head,
The ship drove fast, loud roar'd the blast,
And southward aye we fled.

And now there came both mist and snow,
And it grew wondrous cold :
And ice, mast-high, came floating by,
As green as emerald.

And through the drifts the snowy clifts
Did send a dismal sheen :
Nor shapes of men nor beasts we ken—
The ice was all between.

*The land of ice, and of fearful sounds where no living thing was to be seen.*

The ice was here, the ice was there,
The ice was all around :
It crack'd and growl'd, and roar'd and howl'd,
Like noises in a swound !

At length did cross an Albatross,
Thorough the fog it came ;
As if it had been a Christian soul,*
We hail'd it in God's name.

*Till a great sea-bird, called the Albatross, came through the snow-fog, and was received with great joy and hospitality.*

* And an it were a Christian soul.—1798.

It ate the food it ne'er had eat,*
And round and round it flew.
The ice did split with a thunder-fit ;
The helmsman steer'd us through !

And a good south wind sprung up behind ;
The Albatross did follow,
And every day, for food or play,
Came to the mariner's hollo !

In mist or cloud, on mast or shroud,
It perch'd for vespers nine ;
Whiles all the night, through fog-smoke white,
Glimmer'd the white moon-shine."

" God save thee, ancient Mariner !
From the fiends, that plague thee thus !—
Why look'st thou so ?"—" With my cross-bow
I shot the Albatross.

## PART II.

THE Sun now rose upon the right : †
    Out of the sea came he,
Still hid in mist, and on the left ‡
Went down into the sea.

* The Mariners gave it biscuit-worms.—1798.
† The Sun came up upon the right.—*Ib.*
‡ And broad as a weft upon the left.—*Ib.*

And the good south wind still blew behind,
But no sweet bird did follow,
Nor any day for food or play
Came to the mariners' hollo !

And I had done a hellish thing,
And it would work 'em woe :
For all averr'd, I had kill'd the bird
That made the breeze to blow.
Ah wretch ! said they, the bird to slay,
That made the breeze to blow !

His ship-
mates cry out
against the
ancient Ma-
riner for
killing the
bird of good
luck.

Nor dim nor red, like God's own head,
The glorious Sun uprist :
Then all averr'd, I had kill'd the bird
That brought the fog and mist.
'Twas right, said they, such birds to slay,
That bring the fog and mist.

But when the
fog cleared
off, they jus-
tify the same,
and thus
make them-
selves ac-
complices in
the crime.

The fair breeze blew,* the white foam flew,
The furrow stream'd off free ;†
We were the first that ever burst
Into that silent sea.

The fair
breeze con-
tinues, the
ship enters
the Pacific
Ocean, and
sails north-
ward, even
till it reaches
the Line.

---

* The breezes blew.—1798.

† In the former edition the line was,
        The furrow follow'd free ;
But I had not been long on board a ship before I perceived that this was the image as seen by a spectator
from the shore, or from another vessel. From the
ship itself the *Wake* appears like a brook flowing off
from the stern.  [Note of 1817.]

The ship hath
been sudden-
ly becalmed.

Down dropt the breeze, the sails dropt down,
'Twas sad as sad could be;
And we did speak only to break
The silence of the sea!

All in a hot and copper sky,
The bloody Sun, at noon,
Right up above the mast did stand,
No bigger than the Moon.

Day after day, day after day,
We stuck, nor breath nor motion;
As idle as a painted ship
Upon a painted ocean.

And the Al-
batross be-
gins to be
avenged.

Water, water, every where,
And all the boards did shrink;
Water, water, every where,
Nor any drop to drink.

The very deep did rot: O Christ!
That ever this should be!
Yea, slimy things did crawl with legs
Upon the slimy sea.

About, about, in reel and rout
The death-fires danced at night;
The water, like a witch's oils,
Burnt green and blue and white.

A spirit had
followed
them; one of

And some in dreams assured were
Of the spirit that plagued us so;

Nine fathom deep he had follow'd us
From the Land of Mist and Snow.

the invisible
inhabitants
of this planet,
neither de-
parted souls nor angels ; concerning whom the learned Jew, Josephus, and the
Platonic Constantinopolitan, Michael Psellus, may be consulted.   They are very
numerous, and there is no climate or element without one or more.

And every tongue, through utter drouth,
Was wither'd at the root ;
We could not speak, no more than if
We had been choked with soot.

Ah ! well a-day ! what evil looks
Had I from old and young !
Instead of the Cross, the Albatross
About my neck was hung.

The ship-
mates, in
their sore
distress,
would fain
throw the
whole guilt
on the ancient
Mariner ; in
sign whereof
they hang the
dead sea-bird
round his
neck.

## PART III.

THERE pass'd a weary time.* Each throat
    Was parch'd, and glazed each eye.
A weary time ! a weary time !
How glazed each weary eye,
When looking westward, I beheld
A something in the sky.†

The ancient
Mariner be-
holdeth a sign
in the ele-
ment afar off.

* So pass'd a weary time.—1800.

† In the original version (1798) the Third Part opens :
    " I saw a something in the sky
        No bigger than my fist."

At first it seem'd a little speck,
And then it seem'd a mist;
It moved and moved, and took at last
A certain shape, I wist.

A speck, a mist, a shape, I wist!
And still it near'd and near'd:
And as if it dodged a water-sprite,
It plunged and tack'd and veer'd.

At its nearer approach, it seemeth him to be a ship; and at a dear ransom he freeth his speech from the bonds of thirst.

With throats unslaked, with black lips baked,
We could nor laugh nor wail;
Through utter drought all dumb we stood!*
I bit my arm, I suck'd the blood,
And cried, A sail! a sail!

A flash of joy;

With throats unslaked, with black lips baked,
Agape they heard me call:
Gramercy! they for joy did grin,
And all at once their breath drew in,
As they were drinking all.

And horror follows. For can it be a ship that comes onward without wind or tide?

See! see! (I cried) she tacks no more!†
Hither to work us weal;
Without a breeze, without a tide,‡
She steadies with upright keel!

* Then while thro' drouth all dumb they stood.—1798.

† She doth not tack from side to side.—*Ib.*

‡ Withouten wind, withouten tide.—*Ib.*

The western wave was all a-flame.
The day was well-nigh done !
Almost upon the western wave
Rested the broad bright Sun ;
When that strange shape drove suddenly
Betwixt us and the Sun.

And straight the Sun was fleck'd with bars,
(Heaven's Mother send us grace !)
As if through a dungeon-grate he peer'd
With broad and burning face.

It seemeth him but the skeleton of a ship.

Alas ! (thought I, and my heart beat loud)
How fast she nears and nears !
Are those *her* sails that glance in the Sun,
Like restless gossameres ?

Are those *her* ribs through which the Sun
Did peer, as through a grate ?
And is that Woman all her crew ?
Is that a Death ? and are there two ?
Is Death that woman's mate ?*

And its ribs are seen as bars on the face of the setting Sun. The spectre-woman and her death-mate, and no other on board the skeleton-ship.

* Are those *her* naked ribs, which fleck'd
  The sun that did behind them peer ?
  And are these two all, all the crew,
  That woman and her fleshless Pheere ?—1798.

  Are those *her* ribs which fleck'd the Sun
  Like the bars of a dungeon grate ?
  And are these two all, all the crew
  That woman and her mate ?

[MS. Correction by S. T. C. in a copy of the edition of 1798.]

[This Ship it was a plankless thing,
A bare Anatomy !
A plankless Spectre—and it moved
Like a Being of the Sea !
The woman and a fleshless man
Therein sate merrily.*

His bones were black with many a crack,
All black and bare, I ween ;
Jet-black and bare, save where with rust
Of mouldy damps and charnel crust
They were patch'd† with purple and green.‡]

Like vessel,
like crew !

Her lips were red, her looks were free,
Her locks were yellow as gold :
Her skin was as white as leprosy,
The Night-mare Life-in-Death was she,
Who thicks man's blood with cold.§

Death and
Life-in-death
have diced
for the ship's
crew, and

The naked hulk alongside came,
And the twain were casting dice ;‖

* This stanza was found added in the handwriting
of the Poet in the margin of a copy of the Bristol
edition of *Lyrical Ballads.* It is here printed for the
first time.—Ed.

† They're patch'd.—1798.

‡ The above stanza was omitted by the author
in his own collected editions.—Ed.

§ And she was far liker Death than he ;
    Her flesh made the still air cold.—1800.

‖ Playing dice.—*Ib.*

" The game is done ! I've won, I've won !"
Quoth she, and whistles thrice.

she (the latter) winneth the ancient Mariner.

The Sun's rim dips; the stars rush out :
At one stride comes the dark ;
With far-heard whisper, o'er the sea,
Off shot the spectre-bark.

No twilight within the courts of the sun.

We listen'd and look'd sideways up !
Fear at my heart, as at a cup,
My life-blood seem'd to sip !
The stars were dim, and thick the night,
The steersman's face by his lamp gleam'd white ;
From the sails the dew did drip—
Till clomb above the eastern bar
The horned Moon,* with one bright star
Within the nether tip.

At the rising of the Moon.

One after one, by the star-dogg'd Moon,
Too quick for groan or sigh,
Each turn'd his face with a ghastly pang,
And cursed me with his eye.†

One after another.

* It is a common superstition among sailors that something evil is about to happen whenever a star dogs the moon.—(MS. Note by S. T. C., now first printed.)

† A gust of wind sterte up behind
   And whistled thro' his bones ;
   Thro' the holes of his eyes and the hole of his mouth
   Half-whistles and half-groans.

His ship-
mates drop
down dead.

Four times fifty living men,
(And I heard nor sigh nor groan)\*
With heavy thump, a lifeless lump,
They dropp'd down one by one.

But Life-in-
Death be-
gins her
work on the
ancient Ma-
riner.

Their souls did from their bodies fly,—
They fled to bliss or woe!
And every soul, it pass'd me by,
Like the whizz of my cross-bow!


## PART IV.

The wedding
guest feareth
that a spirit
is talking to
him.

" I FEAR thee, ancient Mariner!
       I fear thy skinny hand!
And thou art long, and lank, and brown,
As is the ribb'd sea-sand.†

With never a whisper in the Sea
Off darts the Spectre-ship;
While clomb above the Eastern bar
The horned Moon, with one bright Star
Almost atween the tips.

One after one by the horned Moon
(Listen, O Stranger! to me)
Each turn'd his face with a ghastly pang
And cursed me with his ee.—1798.

\* With never a sigh or groan.—*Ib.*

† For the last two lines of this stanza I am indebted
to Mr. Wordsworth. It was on a delightful walk
from Nether Stowey to Dulverton, with him and his

I fear thee and thy glittering eye,
And thy skinny hand, so brown."—
Fear not, fear not, thou wedding-guest !
This body dropt not down.

sister, in the autumn of 1797, that this poem was
planned and in part composed.

[" In the autumn of 1797 he (Coleridge), my sister,
and myself started from Alfoxden pretty late in the
afternoon with a view to visit Linton and the Valley of
Stones, near to it. Accordingly we set off and pro-
ceeded along the Quantock Hills towards Watchet,
and in the course of this walk was planned the poem
of *The Ancient Mariner*, founded on a dream, as Mr.
Coleridge said, of his friend Mr. Cruikshank. Much
the greatest part of the story was Mr. Coleridge's invention, but certain parts I suggested : for example, some
crime was to be committed which should bring upon
the Old Navigator, as Coleridge afterwards delighted
to call him, the spectral persecution, as a consequence
of that crime and his own wanderings. I had been
reading in Shelvocke's *Voyages* a day or two before
that, while doubling Cape Horn, they frequently saw
albatrosses in that latitude, the largest sort of sea-fowl,
some extending their wings twelve or thirteen feet.
' Suppose,' said I, ' you represent him as having killed
one of these birds on entering the South Sea, and that
the tutelary spirits of these regions take upon them to
avenge the crime.' The incident was thought fit for
the purpose and adopted accordingly. I also suggested the navigation of the ship by the dead men, but
do not recollect that I had anything more to do with
the scheme of the poem. The gloss with which it
was subsequently accompanied was not thought of by
either of us at the time, at least not a hint of it was

But the ancient Mariner assureth him of his bodily life, and proceedeth to relate his horrible penance.

Alone, alone, all all alone,
Alone on a wide wide sea !
And never a saint took pity on*
My soul in agony.

He despiseth the creatures of the calm.

The many men, so beautiful !
And they all dead did lie :
And a thousand thousand † slimy things
Lived on ; and so did I.

And envieth that they should live, and so many lie dead.

I look'd upon the rotting sea,
And drew my eyes away ;
I look'd upon the rotting deck,‡
And there the dead men lay.

given to me, and I have no doubt it was a gratuitous afterthought. We began the composition together on that, to me, memorable evening. I furnished two or three lines at the beginning of the poem, in particular—

'And listen'd like a three years' child ;
The Mariner had his will.'

These trifling contributions, all but one, which Mr. C. has with unnecessary scrupulosity recorded, slipped out of his mind, as they well might. As we endeavoured to proceed conjointly (I speak of the same evening), our respective manners proved so widely different that it would have been quite presumptuous in me to do anything but separate from an undertaking upon which I could only have been a clog."—WORDSWORTH (see *Memoirs of William Wordsworth*, London, 1851, vol. i., pp. 107-108).]

* Alone on the wide wide Sea ;
And Christ would take no pity on, &c.—1798.

† A million million.—*Ib.*

‡ The eldritch deck.—*Ib.*

I look'd to Heaven, and tried to pray;
But or ever a prayer had gusht,
A wicked whisper came, and made
My heart as dry as dust.

I closed my lids, and kept them close,
And the balls like pulses beat;
For the sky and the sea, and the sea and the sky
Lay like a load on my weary eye,
And the dead were at my feet.

The cold sweat melted from their limbs,
Nor rot nor reek did they:
The look with which they look'd on me
Had never pass'd away.

But the curse
liveth for him
in the eye of
the dead
men.

An orphan's curse would drag to Hell
A spirit from on high;
But oh! more horrible than that
Is the curse in a dead man's eye!
Seven days, seven nights, I saw that curse,
And yet I could not die.

The moving Moon went up the sky,
And no where did abide:
Softly she was going up,
And a star or two beside—

In his loneli-
ness and
fixedness he
yearneth to-
wards the
journeying
Moon, and
the stars that
still sojourn, yet still move onward; and everywhere the blue sky belongs to
them, and is their appointed rest, and their native country and their own natural
homes, which they enter unannounced, as lords that are certainly expected, and
yet there is a silent joy at their arrival.

Her beams bemock'd the sultry main,
Like April hoar-frost spread ;*
But where the ship's huge shadow lay,
The charmed water burnt alway
A still and awful red.

By the light
of the Moon
he beholdeth
God's crea-
tures of the
great calm.

Beyond the shadow of the ship,
I watch'd the water-snakes :
They moved in tracks of shining white,
And when they rear'd, the elfish light
Fell off in hoary flakes.

Within the shadow of the ship
I watch'd their rich attire :
Blue, glossy green, and velvet black,
They coil'd and swam ; and every track
Was a flash of golden fire.

Their beauty
and their
happiness.

O happy living things ! no tongue
Their beauty might declare :
A spring of love gush'd from my heart,

He blesseth
them in his
heart.

And I bless'd them unaware !
Sure my kind saint took pity on me,
And I bless'd them unaware.

The spell be-
gins to break.

The self-same moment I could pray ;
And from my neck so free
The Albatross fell off, and sank
Like lead into the sea.

* Like morning frosts yspread.—1798.

## PART V.

OH sleep ! it is a gentle thing,
    Beloved from pole to pole !
To Mary Queen the praise be given !
She sent the gentle sleep from Heaven,
That slid into my soul.

The silly buckets on the deck,
    That had so long remain'd,
I dreamt that they were fill'd with dew ;
And when I awoke, it rain'd.

*By grace of the holy Mother, the ancient Mariner is refreshed with rain.*

My lips were wet, my throat was cold,
    My garments all were dank ;
Sure I had drunken in my dreams,
And still my body drank.

I moved, and could not feel my limbs :
    I was so light—almost
I thought that I had died in sleep,
And was a blessed ghost.

And soon I heard a roaring wind :*
    It did not come anear ;
But with its sound it shook the sails,
That were so thin and sere.

*He heareth sounds and seeth strange sights and commotions in the sky and the element.*

---

* The roaring wind ! it roar'd far off.—1798.

The upper air burst into life !
And a hundred fire-flags sheen,
To to fro they were hurried about ;
And to and fro, and in and out,
The wan stars danced between. *

And the coming wind did roar more loud,
And the sails did sigh like sedge ;
And the rain pour'd down from one black
  cloud ;
The Moon was at its edge.

The thick black cloud was cleft, and still †
The Moon was at its side :
Like waters shot from some high crag,
The lightning fell with never a jag,
A river steep and wide.

The bodies of the ship's crew are inspirited, and the ship moves on ;

The loud wind never reach'd the ship,
Yet now the ship moved on ! ‡
Beneath the lightning and the moon
The dead men gave a groan.

They groan'd, they stirr'd, they all uprose,
Nor spake, nor moved their eyes ;
It had been strange, even in a dream
To have seen those dead men rise.

* The stars dance on between.—1798.

† Hark ! hark ! the thick black cloud is cleft.—*Ib.*

‡ The strong wind reach'd the ship : it roar'd
 And dropp'd down, like a stone !—*Ib.*

The helmsman steer'd, the ship moved on ;
Yet never a breeze up-blew ;
The mariners all 'gan work the ropes,
Where they were wont to do ;
They raised their limbs like lifeless tools—
We were a ghastly crew.

The body of my brother's son
Stood by me, knee to knee :
The body and I pull'd at one rope,
But he said nought to me.*

"I fear thee, ancient Mariner !"
Be calm, thou Wedding-Guest !
'Twas not those souls that fled in pain,
Which to their corses came again,
But a troop of spirits blest :

But not by
the souls of
the men, nor
by demons of
earth or
middle air,
but by a
blessed troop
of angelic
spirits, sent
down by the
invocation of
the guardian
saint.

For when it dawn'd†—they dropp'd their
    arms,
And cluster'd round the mast ;
Sweet sounds rose slowly through their
    mouths,
And from their bodies pass'd.

* This stanza continues thus in the edition of 1798 :—
    "And I quaked to think of my own voice
        How frightful it would be !"
    The subsequent stanza was added in the edition of
1800.—ED.

    † The day-light dawn'd.—1798.

Around, around, flew each sweet sound,
Then darted to the Sun ;
Slowly the sounds came back again,
Now mix'd, now one by one.

Sometimes a-dropping from the sky
I heard the sky-lark* sing ;
Sometimes all little birds that are,
How they seem'd to fill the sea and air
With their sweet jargoning !

And now 'twas like all instruments,
Now like a lonely flute ;
And now it is an angel's song,
That makes the heavens be mute.

It ceased ; yet still the sails made on
A pleasant noise till noon,
A noise like of a hidden brook
In the leafy month of June,
That to the sleeping woods all night
Singeth a quiet tune.

[Listen, O listen, thou Wedding-Guest !
" Mariner ! thou hast thy will :
For that which comes out of thine eye doth
    make
My body and soul to be still."

---

* I heard the lavrock sing.—1798.

Never sadder tale was told
To a man of woman born :
Sadder and wiser thou Wedding-Guest !
Thou'lt rise to-morrow morn.

Never sadder tale was heard
By a man of woman born :
The Mariners all return'd to work
As silent as beforne.

The Mariners all 'gan pull the ropes,
But look at me they n'old :
Thought I, I am as thin as air—
They cannot me behold." *]

Till noon we quietly sail'd on,†
Yet never a breeze did breathe :
Slowly and smoothly went the ship,
Moved onward from beneath.

Under the keel nine fathom deep,
From the land of mist and snow,
The spirit slid : and it was he
That made the ship to go.
The sails at noon left off their tune,
And the ship stood still also.

The lonesome spirit from the south-pole carries on the ship as far as the line, in obedience to the angelic troop, but still requireth vengeance.

* The above four stanzas only appear in the edition of 1798.—ED.

† Till noon we silently sail'd on.—1798.

The Sun, right up above the mast,
Had fix'd her to the ocean :
But in a minute she 'gan stir,
With a short uneasy motion—
Backwards and forwards half her length
With a short uneasy motion.

Then like a pawing horse let go,
She made a sudden bound :
It flung the blood into my head,
And I fell down in a swound.*

How long in that same fit I lay,
I have not to declare ;
But ere my living life return'd,
I heard, and in my soul discern'd
Two voices in the air.

" Is it he ?" quoth one, " Is this the man ?
By him who died on cross,
With his cruel bow he laid full low
The harmless Albatross.

" The spirit who bideth by himself
In the land of mist and snow,
He loved the bird that loved the man
Who shot him with his bow."

The other was a softer voice,
As soft as honey-dew :

* And I fell into a swound.—1798.

The Polar Spirit's fellow-demons, the invisible inhabitants of the element, take part in his wrong ; and two of them relate, one to the other, that penance long and heavy for the ancient Mariner hath been accorded to the Polar Spirit, who returneth southward.

Quoth he, " The man hath penance done,
And penance more will do."


## PART VI.

### FIRST VOICE.

BUT tell me, tell me ! speak again,
  Thy soft response renewing—
What makes that ship drive on so fast ?
What is the Ocean doing ?

### SECOND VOICE.

Still as a slave before his lord,
The Ocean hath no blast ;
His great bright eye most silently
Up to the Moon is cast—

If he may know which way to go ;
For she guides him smooth or grim.
See, brother, see ! how graciously
She looketh down on him.

### FIRST VOICE.

But why drives on that ship so fast,
Without or wave or wind ?

### SECOND VOICE.

The air is cut away before,
And closes from behind.

The Mariner hath been cast into a trance ; for the angelic power causeth the vessel to drive north-ward faster than human life could endure.

VOL. II.                    E

Fly, brother, fly ! more high, more high !
Or we shall be belated :
For slow and slow that ship will go,
When the Mariner's trance is abated."

The supernatural motion is retarded ; the Mariner awakes, and his penance begins anew.

I woke, and we were sailing on
As in a gentle weather :
'Twas night, calm night, the Moon was high ;
The dead men stood together.

All stood together on the deck,
For a charnel-dungeon fitter :
All fix'd on me their stony eyes,
That in the Moon did glitter.

The pang, the curse, with which they died,
Had never pass'd away :
I could not draw my eyes from theirs,
Nor turn them up to pray.

The curse is finally expiated.

And now this spell was snapt : once more
I view'd the ocean green,
And look'd far forth, yet little saw
Of what had else been seen—*

Like one that on a lonesome † road
Doth walk in fear and dread,

* And in its time the spell was snapt,
    And I could move my een :
  I look'd far-forth, but little saw
    Of what might else be seen.—1798.

† Lonely—*Ib.*

And having once turn'd round, walks on,
And turns no more his head;
Because he knows, a frightful fiend
Doth close behind him tread.

But soon there breathed a wind on me,
Nor sound nor motion made:
Its path was not upon the sea,
In ripple or in shade.

It raised my hair, it fann'd my cheek
Like a meadow-gale of spring—
It mingled strangely with my fears,
Yet it felt like a welcoming.

Swiftly, swiftly flew the ship,
Yet she sail'd softly too:
Sweetly, sweetly blew the breeze—
On me alone it blew.

Oh! dream of joy! is this indeed
The light-house top I see?
Is this the hill? is this the kirk?
Is this mine own countree?

And the ancient Mariner beholdeth his native country.

We drifted o'er the harbour-bar,
And I with sobs did pray—
" O let me be awake, my God!
Or let me sleep alway."

The harbour-bay was clear as glass,
So smoothy it was strewn!

And on the bay the moonlight lay,
And the shadow of the moon.

[The moonlight bay was white all o'er
Till rising from the same
Full many shapes, that shadows were,
Like as of torches came.

A little distance from the prow
Those dark-red shadows were;
But soon I saw that my own flesh
Was red as in a glare.

I turn'd my head in fear and dread,
And by the holy rood
The bodies had advanced, and now
Before the mast they stood.

They lifted up their stiff right arms,
They held them straight and tight;
And each right-arm burnt like a torch,
A torch that's borne upright.
Their stony eyeballs glitter'd on
In the red and smoky light.

I pray'd and turn'd my head away
Forth looking as before.
There was no breeze upon the bay,
No wave against the shore.]*

* The above five stanzas are only in the edition of
1798.—ED.

The rock shone bright, the kirk no less,
That stands above the rock :
The moonlight steep'd in silentness
The steady weathercock.

And the bay was white with silent light,
Till rising from the same,
Full many shapes, that shadows were,    The angelic
In crimson colours came.                spirits leave
                                        the dead
                                        bodies,

A little distance from the prow          And appear
Those crimson shadows were :             in their own
I turn'd my eyes upon the deck—          forms of light.
Oh, Christ ! what saw I there !

Each corse lay flat, lifeless and flat,
And, by the holy rood !
A man all light, a seraph-man,
On every corse there stood.

This seraph-band, each waved his hand :
It was a heavenly sight !
They stood as signals to the land,
Each one a lovely light :

This seraph-band, each waved his hand,
No voice did they impart—
No voice ; but oh ! the silence sank
Like music on my heart.

But soon I heard the dash of oars,
I heard the Pilot's cheer ;

My head was turn'd perforce away,
And I saw a boat appear.

[Then vanish'd all the lovely lights ;
The bodies rose anew :
With silent pace, each to his place,
Came back the ghastly crew.
The wind that shade nor motion made
On me alone it blew.]*

The Pilot and the Pilot's boy,
I heard them coming fast :
Dear Lord in Heaven ! it was a joy
The dead men could not blast.

I saw a third—I heard his voice :
It is the Hermit good !
He singeth loud his godly hymns
That he makes in the wood.
He'll shrieve my soul, he'll wash away
The Albatross's blood.

* This stanza only appears in the edition of 1798.
In a copy of that edition the stanza is marked through,
and the following lines are substituted in the margin
in the handwriting of the author :—

"Then vanish'd all the lovely lights,
    The spirits of the air,
    No souls of mortal men were they,
    But spirits bright and fair."

## PART VII.

THIS Hermit good lives in that wood   The Hermit
    Which slopes down to the sea.       of the wood
How loudly his sweet voice he rears !
He loves to talk with marineres
That come from a far countree.

He kneels at morn, and noon, and eve—
He hath a cushion plump :
It is the moss that wholly hides
The rotted old oak-stump.

The skiff-boat near'd : I heard them talk,
" Why, this is strange, I trow !
Where are those lights so many and fair,
That signal made but now ?"

" Strange, by my faith !" the Hermit said—   Approacheth
" And they answer'd not our cheer !         the ship with
The planks look warp'd ! and see those sails,  wonder.
How thin they are and sere !
I never saw aught like to them,
Unless perchance it were

Brown skeletons * of leaves that lag
My forest-brook along ;

* The skeletons.—1798-1817.

When the ivy-tod is heavy with snow,
And the owlet whoops to the wolf below,
That eats the she-wolf's young."

" Dear Lord ! it hath a fiendish look—
(The Pilot made reply)
I am a-fear'd"—" Push on, push on !"
Said the Hermit cheerily.

The boat came closer to the ship,
But I nor spake nor stirr'd ;
The boat came close beneath the ship,
And straight a sound was heard.

The ship suddenly sinketh.

Under the water it rumbled on,
Still louder and more dread :
It reach'd the ship, it split the bay ;
The ship went down like lead.

The ancient Mariner is saved in the Pilot's boat.

Stunn'd by that loud and dreadful sound,
Which sky and ocean smote,
Like one that hath been seven days drown'd
My body lay afloat ;
But swift as dreams, myself I found
Within the Pilot's boat.

Upon the whirl, where sank the ship,
The boat spun round and round ;
And all was still, save that the hill
Was telling of the sound.

I moved my lips—the Pilot shriek'd
And fell down in a fit ;

The holy Hermit raised his eyes,
And pray'd where he did sit.

I took the oars : the Pilot's boy,
Who now doth crazy go,
Laugh'd loud and long, and all the while
His eyes went to and fro.
" Ha ! ha !" quoth he, " full plain I see
The Devil knows how to row."

And now, all in my own countree,
I stood on the firm land !
The Hermit stepp'd forth from the boat,
And scarcely he could stand.

" O shrieve me, shrieve me, holy man !"
The Hermit cross'd his brow.
" Say quick," quoth he, " I bid thee say—
What manner of man art thou ?"

The ancient Mariner earnestly entreateth the Hermit to shrieve him ; and the penance of life falls on him.

Forthwith this frame of mine was wrench'd
With a woful agony,
Which forced me to begin my tale ;
And then it left me free.

Since then, at an uncertain hour,
That agony returns :
And till my ghastly tale is told,
This heart within me burns.*

And ever and anon throughout his future life an agony constraineth him to travel from land to land ;

* Since then at an uncertain hour
   Now ofttimes and now fewer,
   That anguish comes and makes me tell
   My ghastly aventure.—1798.

I pass, like night, from land to land ;
I have strange power of speech ;
The moment that his face I see,
I know the man that must hear me :
To him my tale I teach.

What loud uproar bursts from that door !
The wedding-guests are there :
But in the garden-bower the bride
And bride-maids singing are :
And hark the little vesper bell,
Which biddeth me to prayer !

O Wedding-Guest ! this soul hath been
Alone on a wide wide sea :
So lonely 'twas, that God himself
Scarce seemed there to be.

O sweeter than the marriage-feast,
'Tis sweeter far to me,
To walk together to the kirk
With a goodly company !—

To walk together to the kirk,
And all together pray,
While each to his great Father bends,
Old men, and babes, and loving friends,
And youths and maidens gay !

And to teach,
by his own
example,
love and re-

Farewell, farewell ! but this I tell
To thee, thou Wedding-Guest !

He prayeth well who loveth well
Both man and bird and beast.

verence to all
things that
God made
and loveth.

He prayeth best, who loveth best
All things both great and small ;
For the dear God who loveth us,
He made and loveth all."

The Mariner, whose eye is bright,
Whose beard with age is hoar,
Is gone : and now the Wedding-Guest
Turn'd from the bridegroom's door.

He went like one that hath been stunn'd,
And is of sense forlorn :
A sadder and a wiser man
He rose the morrow morn.

# CHRISTABEL.

## [1797-1800.]

[The Fragment of *Christabel*, although communicated to many friends in MS. during the previous eighteen years, was not printed till 1816, when it was published by Mr. Murray of Albemarle-street, as a thin octavo of 64 pages in conjunction with *Kubla Khan, a Vision*, and *The Pains of Sleep*.

Some years before that publication two of the MS. copies of *Christabel* alluded to came under the inspection and one of them into the possession of Mr. J. Payne Collier, who in the volume entitled *Seven Lectures on Shakespeare and Milton, by the late S. T. Coleridge*, edited by him in 1856, has noticed (pp. xxxix-xliii) a few verbal differences between these and the published version.—ED.]

# CHRISTABEL.

## PREFACE.

THE first part of the following poem was written in the year 1797, at Stowey, in the county of Somerset. The second part, after my return from Germany, in the year 1800, at Keswick, Cumberland. Since the latter date my poetic powers have been, till very lately, in a state of suspended animation. But as, in my very first conception of the tale, I had the whole present to my mind with the wholeness no less than with the liveliness of a vision, I trust that I shall be able to embody in verse the three parts yet to come in the course of the present year. It is probable that if the poem had been finished at either of the former periods, or if even the first and second part had been published in the year 1800, the impression of its originality would have been much greater than I dare at present expect. But for this I have only my own indolence to blame. The dates are mentioned for the exclusive purpose of precluding charges of plagiarism or servile imitation from myself. For there is amongst us a set of critics who seem to hold that every possible thought and image is traditional; who have no notion that there are such things as fountains in the world, small as well as great; and who would therefore charitably derive every rill they behold flowing from a perforation made in some other man's tank. I am confident, however, that as far as the present poem is concerned, the celebrated poets whose writings I might be suspected of having imitated, either in particular passages or in the tone and the spirit of the whole, would be among the first to vindicate me from the charge, and who, on any striking coincidence, would permit me to address them in this doggerel version of two monkish Latin hexameters:

'Tis mine and it is likewise yours;
But an if this will not do;
Let it be mine, good friend! for I
Am the poorer of the two.

I have only to add that the metre of the *Christabel* is not, properly speaking, irregular, though it may seem so from its being founded on a new principle—namely, that of counting in each line the accents, not the syllables. Though the latter may vary from seven to twelve, yet in each line the accents will be found to be only four. Nevertheless this occasional variation in number of syllables is not introduced wantonly, or for the mere ends of convenience, but in correspondence with some transition in the nature of the imagery or passion.

[1816.]

## PART I.

'TIS the middle of night by the castle clock,
      And the owls have awaken'd the crowing
            cock,
Tu—whit!——Tu—whoo!
And hark, again! the crowing cock,
How drowsily it crew.

Sir Leoline, the Baron rich,
Hath a toothless mastiff bitch ;
From her kennel beneath the rock
She * maketh answer to the clock,†
Four for the quarters, and twelve for the hour ;
Ever and aye, by shine and shower,‡
Sixteen short howls, not over loud ;
Some say, she sees my lady's shroud.

Is the night chilly and dark ?
The night is chilly, but not dark.
The thin gray cloud is spread on high,
It covers but not hides the sky.
The moon is behind, and at the full ;
And yet she looks both small and dull.
The night is chill, the cloud is gray :
'Tis a month before the month of May,
And the Spring comes slowly up this way.

The lovely lady, Christabel,
Whom her father loves so well,
What makes her in the wood so late,
A furlong from the castle gate ?
She had dreams all yesternight
Of her own betrothed knight ;
[Dreams that made her moan and leap
As on her bed she lay in sleep ;]

* Makes answer—1816.
† Hath a toothless mastiff, which
  From her kennel beneath the rock
  Maketh answer to the clock—1829.
‡ Moonshine or shower—1816.

And she in the midnight wood will pray
For the weal of her lover that's far away.

She stole along, she nothing spoke,
The sighs she heaved were soft and low,*
And nought was green upon the oak
But moss and rarest misletoe :
She kneels beneath the huge oak tree,
And in silence prayeth she.

The lady sprang up† suddenly,
The lovely lady, Christabel !
It moan'd as near as near can be,
But what it is she cannot tell.—
On the other side it seems to be
Of the huge, broad-breasted, old oak tree.

The night is chill; the forest bare ;
Is it the wind that moaneth bleak ?
There is not wind enough in the air
To move away the ringlet curl
From the lovely lady's cheek—
There is not wind enough to twirl
The one red leaf, the last of its clan,
That dances as often as dance it can,
Hanging so light, and hanging so high,
On the topmost twig that looks up at the sky.

* The breezes they were still also—1816.
    The breezes they were whispering low—
                [S. T. C., MS. Copy, lent to
                        Mr. Payne Collier in 1811.]
† Leaps up—1816.

Hush, beating heart of Christabel!
Jesu Maria, shield her well!
She folded her arms beneath her cloak,
And stole to the other side of the oak.
    What sees she there?

There she sees a damsel bright,
Drest in a silken robe of white,
*That shadowy in the moonlight shone :
The neck that made that white robe wan,
Her stately neck and arms were bare ;
Her blue-vein'd feet unsandal'd were,
And wildly glitter'd here and there
The gems entangled in her hair.
I guess, 'twas frightful there to see
A lady so richly clad as she—
Beautiful exceedingly!

" Mary mother, save me now ! "
(Said Christabel,) " And who art thou ? "

The lady strange made answer meet,
And her voice was faint and sweet :—
" Have pity on my sore distress,
I scarce can speak for weariness :
Stretch forth thy hand, and have no fear ! "
Said Christabel, " How camest thou here ? "
And the lady, whose voice was faint and sweet,
Did thus pursue her answer meet :—

* Her neck, her feet, her arms were bare,
  And the jewels disorder'd in her hair.—1816.

" My sire is of a noble line,
And my name is Geraldine :
Five warriors * seized me yestermorn,
Me, even me, a maid forlorn :
They choked my cries with force and fright,
And tied me on a palfrey white.
The palfrey was as fleet as wind,
And they rode furiously behind.
They spurr'd amain, their steeds were white :
And once we cross'd the shade of night.
As sure as Heaven shall rescue me,
I have no thought what men they be ;
Nor do I know how long it is
(For I have lain entranced I wis) †
Since one, the tallest of the five,
Took me from the palfrey's back,
A weary woman, scarce alive.
Some mutter'd words his comrades spoke :
He placed me underneath this oak ;
He swore they would return with haste ;
Whither they went I cannot tell—
I thought I heard, some minutes past,
Sounds as of a castle bell.
Stretch forth thy hand" (thus ended she),
"And help a wretched maid to flee."

* " Five ruffians" in Mr. Collier's Salisbury MS.    This
was a copy of *Christabel* made by a lady of Salisbury, Miss
Stoddart, who afterwards became the wife of William Hazlitt.

† (For I have lain in fits, I wis)—1816.

Then Christabel stretch'd forth her hand,
And comforted fair Geraldine:
*"O well, bright dame! may you command
The service of Sir Leoline;
And gladly our stout chivalry
Will he send forth and friends withal
To guide and guard you safe and free
Home to your noble father's hall."

†She rose: and forth with steps they pass'd
That strove to be, and were not, fast.
Her gracious stars the lady blest,
And thus spake on sweet Christabel:
"All our household are at rest,
The hall as silent as the cell; ‡

   * Saying, that she should command
     The service of Sir Leoline;
     And straight be convoy'd, free from thrall,
     Back to her noble father's hall.—1816.

   † So up she rose: and forth they pass'd
     With hurrying steps, yet nothing fast;
     Her lucky stars the lady blest,
     And Christabel she sweetly said—
   "All our household are at rest,
     Each one sleeping in his bed;
     Sir Leoline is weak in health,
     And may not well awaken'd be,
     So to my room we'll creep in stealth,
     And you to-night must sleep with me."—*Ib.*

   ‡ Her smiling stars the lady blest,
     And thus bespake sweet Christabel:
   "All our household is at rest,
     The hall as silent as a cell."
[MS. Copy lent by S. T. C. to Mr. Payne Collier in 1811.]

Sir Leoline is weak in health,
And may not well awaken'd be,
But we will move as if in stealth,
And I beseech your courtesy,
This night, to share your couch with me."

They cross'd the moat, and Christabel
Took the key that fitted well;
A little door she open'd straight,
All in the middle of the gate;
The gate that was iron'd within and without,
Where an army in battle array had march'd out.
The lady sank, belike through pain,
And Christabel with might and main
Lifted her up, a weary weight,
Over the threshold of the gate:
Then the lady rose again,
And moved, as she were not in pain.

So free from danger, free from fear,
They cross'd the court: right glad they were.
And Christabel devoutly cried
To the lady by her side;
" Praise we the Virgin all divine
Who hath rescued thee from thy distress!"
"Alas, alas!" said Geraldine,
" I cannot speak for weariness."
So free from danger, free from fear,
They cross'd the court: right glad they were.

Outside her kennel the mastiff old
Lay fast asleep, in moonshine cold.

The mastiff old did not awake,
Yet she an angry moan did make !
And what can ail the mastiff bitch ?
Never till now she utter'd yell
Beneath the eye of Christabel.
Perhaps it is the owlet's scritch :
For what can ail the mastiff bitch ?

They pass'd the hall, that echoes still,
Pass as lightly as you will !
The brands were flat, the brands were dying,
Amid their own white ashes lying ;
But when the lady pass'd, there came
A tongue of light, a fit of flame ;
And Christabel saw the lady's eye,
And nothing else saw she thereby,
Save the boss of the shield of Sir Leoline tall,
Which hung in a murky old niche in the wall.
" O softly tread," said Christabel,
" My father seldom sleepeth well."

Sweet Christabel her feet doth bare,
And, jealous of the listening air,
They steal their way from stair to stair,*
Now in glimmer, and now in gloom,
And now they pass the Baron's room,
As still as death, with stifled breath !
And now have reach'd her chamber door ;

* Sweet Christabel her feet she bares,
    And they are creeping up the stairs ;—1816.

And now doth Geraldine press down
The rushes of the chamber floor.*

The moon shines dim in the open air,
And not a moonbeam enters here.
But they without its light can see
The chamber carved so curiously,
Carved with figures strange and sweet,
All made out of the carver's brain,
For a lady's chamber meet:
The lamp with twofold silver chain
Is fasten'd to an angel's feet.

The silver lamp burns dead and dim;
But Christabel the lamp will trim.
She trimm'd the lamp, and made it bright,
And left it swinging to and fro,
While Geraldine, in wretched plight,
Sank down upon the floor below.

" O weary lady, Geraldine,
I pray you, drink this cordial wine ! †
It is a wine of virtuous powers ;
My mother made it of wild flowers."

"And will your mother pity me,
Who am a maiden most forlorn ? "

---

\* And now with eager feet press down
    The rushes of her chamber floor.—1816.

† Here followed these two lines in Mr. Payne Collier's
Salisbury MS. :—

    " Nay, drink it up ; I pray you do :
    Believe me, it will comfort you."

Christabel answer'd—"Woe is me!
She died the hour that I was born.
I have heard the grey-hair'd friar tell
How on her death-bed she did say
That she should hear the castle-bell
Strike twelve upon my wedding-day.
O mother dear! that thou wert here!"
"I would," said Geraldine, "she were!"

But soon with alter'd voice, said she—
"Off, wandering mother! Peak and pine!
I have power to bid thee flee."
Alas! what ails poor Geraldine?
Why stares she with unsettled eye?
Can she the bodiless dead espy?
And why with hollow voice cries she,
"Off, woman, off! this hour is mine—
Though thou her guardian spirit be,
Off, woman, off! 'tis given to me."

Then Christabel knelt by the lady's side,
And raised to heaven her eyes so blue—
"Alas!" said she, "this ghastly ride—
Dear lady! it hath wilder'd you!"
The lady wiped her moist cold brow,
And faintly said, "'Tis over now!"*

Again the wild-flower wine she drank:
Her fair large eyes 'gan glitter bright,

* And faintly said, "I'm better now."
[Mr. Collier's Salisbury MS.]

And from the floor whereon she sank,
The lofty lady stood upright:
She was most beautiful to see,
Like a lady of a far countrée.

And thus the lofty lady spake—
" All they who live in the upper sky,
Do love you, holy Christabel!
And you love them, and for their sake
And for the good which me befel,
Even I in my degree will try,
Fair maiden, to requite you well.
But now unrobe yourself; for I
Must pray, ere yet in bed I lie."

Quoth Christabel, " So let it be!"
And as the lady bade, did she.
Her gentle limbs did she undress,
And lay down in her loveliness.

But through her brain of weal and woe
So many thoughts moved to and fro,
That vain it were her lids to close;
So half-way from the bed she rose,
And on her elbow did recline
To look at the lady Geraldine.

Beneath the lamp the lady bow'd,
And slowly roll'd her eyes around;
Then drawing in her breath aloud
Like one that shudder'd, she unbound

The cincture from beneath her breast :
Her silken robe, and inner vest,
Dropt to her feet, and full in view,
Behold ! her bosom and half her side——
A sight to dream of, not to tell !
O shield her ! shield sweet Christabel !*

† Yet Geraldine nor speaks nor stirs ;
Ah ! what a stricken look was hers !
Deep from within she seems half-way
To lift some weight with sick assay,
And eyes the maid and seeks delay ;
Then suddenly, as one defied,
Collects herself in scorn and pride,
And lay down by the maiden's side !—
And in her arms the maid she took,
      Ah wel-a-day !
And with low voice and doleful look
These words did say :
"In the touch of this bosom there worketh a spell,
Which is lord of thy utterance, Christabel !
Thou knowest to-night, and wilt know to-morrow,
This mark of my shame, this seal of my sorrow ;
    But vainly thou warrest,
      For this is alone in
    Thy power to declare,
      That in the dim forest
    Thou heard'st a low moaning,

* And she is to sleep by Christabel.—1816.
† She took two paces, and a stride,
  And lay down by the maiden's side :—*Ib.*

And found'st a bright lady, surpassingly fair ;
And didst bring her home with thee in love and
　　in charity,
To shield her and shelter her from the damp air."


## THE CONCLUSION

### TO PART I.

IT was a lovely sight to see
The lady Christabel, when she
Was praying at the old oak tree.
　　Amid the jagged shadows
　　Of mossy leafless boughs
　　Kneeling in the moonlight
　　To make her gentle vows ;
Her slender palms together prest,
Heaving sometimes on her breast ;
Her face resign'd to bliss or bale—
Her face, oh call it fair not pale,
And both blue eyes more bright than clear
Each about to have a tear.

With open eyes (ah woe is me !)
Asleep, and dreaming fearfully,
Fearfully dreaming, yet, I wis,
Dreaming that alone which is—
O sorrow and shame !　Can this be she,
The lady who knelt at the old oak tree ?
And lo ! the worker of these harms,
That holds the maiden in her arms,

Seems to slumber still and mild,
As a mother with her child.

A star hath set, a star hath risen,
O Geraldine ! since arms of thine
Have been the lovely lady's prison.
O Geraldine ! one hour was thine—
Thou'st had thy will !   By tairn and rill,
The night-birds all that hour were still.
But now they are jubilant anew,
From cliff and tower, tu— whoo ! tu—whoo !
Tu—whoo ! tu—whoo ! from wood and fell.

And see ! the lady Christabel
Gathers herself from out her trance ;
Her limbs relax, her countenance
Grows sad and soft ; the smooth thin lids
Close o'er her eyes ; and tears she sheds—
Large tears that leave the lashes bright !
And oft the while she seems to smile
As infants at a sudden light !

Yea, she doth smile, and she doth weep,
Like a youthful hermitess,
Beauteous in a wilderness,
Who, praying always, prays in sleep.
And, if she move unquietly,
Perchance, 'tis but the blood so free
Comes back and tingles in her feet.
No doubt she hath a vision sweet.
What if her guardian spirit 'twere ?
What if she knew her mother near ?

But this she knows, in joys and woes,
That saints will aid if men will call :
For the blue sky bends over all !


## PART II.

"EACH matin bell," the Baron saith,
    "Knells us back to a world of death."
These words Sir Leoline first said
When he rose and found his lady dead :
These words Sir Leoline will say
Many a morn to his dying day.

And hence the custom and law began
That still at dawn the sacristan,
Who duly pulls the heavy bell,
Five and forty beads must tell
Between each stroke—a warning knell,
Which not a soul can choose but hear
From Bratha Head to Windermere.

Saith Bracy the bard, "So let it knell !
And let the drowsy sacristan
Still count as slowly as he can !
There is no lack of such, I ween,
As well fill up the space between.
In Langdale Pike and Witch's Lair,
And Dungeon-ghyll so foully rent,
With ropes of rock and bells of air
Three sinful sextons' ghosts are pent,

Who all give back, one after t'other,
The death-note to their living brother;
And oft too, by the knell offended,
Just as their one! two! three! is ended,
The devil mocks the doleful tale
With a merry peal from Borrowdale."

The air is still! through mist and cloud
That merry peal comes ringing loud;
And Geraldine shakes off her dread,
And rises lightly from the bed;
Puts on her silken vestments white,
And tricks her hair in lovely plight,
And nothing doubting of her spell
Awakens the lady Christabel.
" Sleep you, sweet lady Christabel?
I trust that you have rested well."

And Christabel awoke and spied
The same who lay down by her side—
O rather say, the same whom she
Raised up beneath the old oak tree!
Nay, fairer yet! and yet more fair!
For she belike hath drunken deep
Of all the blessedness of sleep!
And while she spake, her looks, her air,
Such gentle thankfulness declare,
That (so it seem'd) her girded vests
Grew tight beneath her heaving breasts.
" Sure I have sinn'd!" said Christabel,
" Now heaven be praised if all be well!"

And in low faltering tones, yet sweet,
Did she the lofty lady greet
With such perplexity of mind
As dreams too lively leave behind.

So quickly she rose, and quickly array'd
Her maiden limbs, and having pray'd
That he who on the cross did groan
Might wash away her sins unknown,
She forthwith led fair Geraldine
To meet her sire, Sir Leoline.

The lovely maid and the lady tall
Are pacing both into the hall,
And pacing on through page and groom,
Enter the Baron's presence-room.

The Baron rose, and while he prest
His gentle daughter to his breast,
With cheerful wonder in his eyes
The lady Geraldine espies,
And gave such welcome to the same
As might beseem so bright a dame!

But when he heard the lady's tale,
And when she told her father's name,
Why wax'd Sir Leoline so pale,
Murmuring o'er the name again,
Lord Roland de Vaux of Tryermaine?

Alas! they had been friends in youth;
But whispering tongues can poison truth;

And constancy lives in realms above;
And life is thorny; and youth is vain;
And to be wroth with one we love
Doth work like madness in the brain.
And thus it chanced, as I divine,
With Roland and Sir Leoline.
Each spake words of high disdain
And insult to his heart's best brother:
They parted—ne'er to meet again!
But never either found another
To free the hollow heart from paining—
They stood aloof, the scars remaining,
Like cliffs which had been rent asunder;
A dreary sea now flows between;—
But neither heat, nor frost, nor thunder,
Shall wholly do away, I ween,
The marks of that which once hath been.

Sir Leoline, a moment's space,
Stood gazing on the damsel's face:
And the youthful Lord of Tryermaine
Came back upon his heart again.

O then the Baron forgot his age,
His noble heart swell'd high with rage;
He swore by the wounds in Jesu's side
He would proclaim it far and wide,
With trump and solemn heraldry,
That they who thus had wrong'd the dame
Were base as spotted infamy!
" And if they dare deny the same,

My herald shall appoint a week,
And let the recreant traitors seek
My tourney court—that there and then
I may dislodge their reptile souls
From the bodies and forms of men!"
He spake: his eye in lightning rolls!
For the lady was ruthlessly seized; and he kenn'd
In the beautiful lady the child of his friend!

And now the tears were on his face,
And fondly in his arms he took
Fair Geraldine, who met the embrace,
Prolonging it with joyous look.
Which when she view'd, a vision fell
Upon the soul of Christabel,
The vision of fear, the touch and pain!*
She shrunk and shudder'd, and saw again—
(Ah, woe is me! Was it for thee,
Thou gentle maid! such sights to see?)
Again she saw that bosom old,
Again she felt that bosom cold,
And drew in her breath with a hissing sound:
Whereat the Knight turn'd wildly round,
And nothing saw, but his own sweet maid
With eyes upraised, as one that pray'd.

The touch, the sight, had pass'd away,†
And in its stead that vision blest,

---

* The vision foul of fear and pain!
                    [Mr. Collier's Salisbury MS.]
† The pang, the sight, was past away—*ib.*

Which comforted her after-rest,
While in the lady's arms she lay,
Had put a rapture in her breast,
And on her lips and o'er her eyes
Spread smiles like light !

      With new surprise,
" What ails then my beloved child?"
The Baron said—His daughter mild
Made answer, " All will yet be well !"
I ween, she had no power to tell
Aught else : so mighty was the spell.

Yet he, who saw this Geraldine,
Had deem'd her sure a thing divine.
Such sorrow with such grace she blended,
As if she fear'd she had offended
Sweet Christabel, that gentle maid !
And with such lowly tones she pray'd
She might be sent without delay
Home to her father's mansion.

        " Nay !
Nay, by my soul !" said Leoline.
" Ho ! Bracy, the bard, the charge be thine !
Go thou, with music sweet and loud,
And take two steeds with trappings proud,
And take the youth whom thou lovest best
To bear thy harp, and learn thy song,
And clothe you both in solemn vest,
And over the mountains haste along,
Lest wandering folk, that are abroad,
Detain you on the valley road.

"And when he has cross'd the Irthing flood,
My merry bard ! he hastes, he hastes
Up Knorren Moor, through Halegarth Wood,
And reaches soon that castle good
Which stands and threatens Scotland's wastes.

" Bard Bracy ! bard Bracy ! your horses are fleet,
Ye must ride up the hall, your music so sweet,
More loud than your horses' echoing feet !
And loud and loud to Lord Roland call,
' Thy daughter is safe in Langdale hall !
Thy beautiful daughter is safe and free—.
Sir Leoline greets thee thus through me.
He bids thee come without delay
With all thy numerous array ;
And take thy lovely daughter home :
And he will meet thee on the way
With all his numerous array
White with their panting palfreys' foam :'
And, by mine honour ! I will say,
That I repent me of the day
When I spake words of fierce disdain
To Roland de Vaux of Tryermaine !—
—For since that evil hour hath flown,
Many a summer's sun hath shone ;
Yet ne'er found I a friend again
Like Roland de Vaux of Tryermaine."

The lady fell, and clasp'd his knees,
Her face upraised, her eyes o'erflowing ;

And Bracy replied, with faltering voice,
His gracious hail on all bestowing :—
"Thy words, thou sire of Christabel,
Are sweeter than my harp can tell ;
Yet might I gain a boon of thee,
This day my journey should not be.
So strange a dream hath come to me
That I had vow'd with music loud
To clear yon wood from thing unblest,
Warn'd by a vision in my rest !
For in my sleep I saw that dove,
That gentle bird whom thou dost love,
And call'st by thy own daughter's name—
Sir Leoline ! I saw the same
Fluttering, and uttering fearful moan,
Among the green herbs in the forest alone.
Which when I saw and when I heard,
I wonder'd what might ail the bird ;
For nothing near it could I see,
Save the grass and green herbs underneath the
    old tree.

"And in my dream methought I went
To search out what might there be found ;
And what the sweet bird's trouble meant,
That thus lay fluttering on the ground.
I went and peer'd, and could descry
No cause for her distressful cry ;
But yet for her dear lady's sake
I stoop'd, methought, the dove to take,
When lo ! I saw a bright green snake

Coil'd around its wings and neck.
Green as the herbs on which it couch'd,
Close by the dove's its head it crouch'd ;
And with the dove it heaves and stirs,
Swelling its neck as she swell'd hers !
I woke ; it was the midnight hour,
The clock was echoing in the tower ;
But though my slumber was gone by,
This dream it would not pass away—
It seems to live upon my eye !
And thence I vow'd this self-same day
With music strong and saintly song,
To wander through the forest bare,
Lest aught unholy loiter there."

Thus Bracy said : the Baron, the while,
Half-listening heard him with a smile ;
Then turn'd to Lady Geraldine,
His eyes made up of wonder and love ;
And said in courtly accents fine,
" Sweet maid, Lord Ronald's beauteous dove,
With arms more strong than harp or song,
Thy sire and I will crush the snake !"
He kiss'd her forehead as he spake,
And Geraldine in maiden wise
Casting down her large bright eyes,
With blushing cheek and courtesy fine
She turn'd her from Sir Leoline ;
Softly gathering up her train,
That o'er her right arm fell again ;
And folded her arms across her chest,

And couch'd her head upon her breast,
And looked askance at Christabel——
Jesu Maria, shield her well!

A snake's small eye blinks dull and shy,
And the lady's eyes they shrunk in her head,
Each shrunk up to a serpent's eye,
And with somewhat of malice, and more of dread,
At Christabel she look'd askance!——
One moment—and the sight was fled!
But Christabel, in dizzy trance
Stumbling on the unsteady ground—
Shudder'd aloud, with a hissing sound;
And Geraldine again turn'd round,
And like a thing that sought relief,
Full of wonder and full of grief,
She roll'd her large bright eyes divine
Wildly on Sir Leoline.

The maid, alas! her thoughts are gone,
She nothing sees—no sight but one!
The maid, devoid of guile and sin,
I know not how, in fearful wise,
So deeply had she drunken in
That look, those shrunken serpent eyes,
That all her features were resign'd
To this sole image in her mind;
And passively did imitate
That look of dull and treacherous hate.
And thus she stood, in dizzy trance,
Still picturing that look askance

With forced unconscious sympathy
Full before her father's view——
As far as such a look could be
In eyes so innocent and blue !

And, when the trance was o'er,* the maid
Paused awhile, and inly pray'd :
Then falling at the Baron's feet,†
" By my mother's soul do I entreat
That thou this woman send away !"
She said : and more she could not say :
For what she knew she could not tell,
O'er-master'd by the mighty spell.

Why is thy cheek so wan and wild,
Sir Leoline ? Thy only child
Lies at thy feet, thy joy, thy pride,
So fair, so innocent, so mild ;
The same, for whom thy lady died !
O, by the pangs of her dear mother
Think thou no evil of thy child !
For her, and thee, and for no other,
She pray'd the moment ere she died :
Pray'd that the babe, for whom she died,
Might prove her dear lord's joy and pride !
That prayer her deadly pangs beguiled,
Sir Leoline !
And wouldst thou wrong thy only child,
Her child and thine ?

---

* But when the trance was o'er—1816.

† Then falling at her father's feet—*ib.*

Within the Baron's heart and brain
If thoughts like these had any share,
They only swell'd his rage and pain,
And did but work confusion there.
His heart was cleft with pain and rage,
His cheeks they quiver'd, his eyes were wild,
Dishonour'd thus in his old age;
Dishonour'd by his only child,
And all his hospitality
To the wrong'd daughter* of his friend
By more than woman's jealousy
Brought thus to a disgraceful end—
He roll'd his eye with stern regard
Upon the gentle minstrel bard,
And said in tones abrupt, austere—
" Why, Bracy ! dost thou loiter here ?
I bade thee hence !" The bard obey'd ;
And, turning from his own sweet maid,
The aged knight, Sir Leoline,
Led forth the lady Geraldine !


# THE CONCLUSION

## TO PART II.

A LITTLE child, a limber elf,
Singing, dancing to itself,
A fairy thing with red round cheeks,
That always finds, and never seeks,

---

\* To th' insulted daughter—1816.

Makes such a vision to the sight
As fills a father's eyes with light;
And pleasures flow in so thick and fast
Upon his heart, that he at last
Must needs express his love's excess
With words of unmeant bitterness.
Perhaps 'tis pretty to force together
Thoughts so all unlike each other;
To mutter and mock a broken charm,
To dally with wrong that does no harm.
Perhaps 'tis tender too and pretty
At each wild word to feel within
A sweet recoil of love and pity.
And what if in a world of sin
(O sorrow and shame should this be true!)
Such giddiness of heart and brain
Comes seldom save from rage and pain,
So talks as it's most used to do.

# INTRODUCTION TO THE TALE OF THE DARK LADIE.*

[To the Editor of the *Morning Post*.

Sir,

The following Poem is the Introduction to a somewhat longer one, for which I shall solicit insertion on your next open day. The use of the old Ballad word *Ladie*, for Lady, is the only piece of obsoleteness in it; and as it is professedly a tale of ancient times, I trust that " the affectionate lovers of venerable antiquity" (as Camden says) will grant me their pardon, and perhaps may be induced to admit a force and propriety in it. A heavier objection may be adduced against the Author, that in these times of fear and expectation, when novelties *explode* around us in all directions, he should presume to offer to the public a silly tale of old-fashioned love; and five years ago, I own, I should have allowed and felt the force of this objection. But, alas! explosion has succeeded explosion so rapidly that novelty itself ceases to appear new; and it is possible that now, even a simple story wholly unspiced with politics or personality, may find some attention amid the hubbub of Revolutions, as to those who have remained a long time by the falls of Niagara, the lowest whispering becomes distinctly audible.

S. T. COLERIDGE.]

* *Morning Post*, December 21, 1799.—The substance of this poem (with the omission of the four opening and three concluding stanzas) appeared in the second edition of *Lyrical Ballads* (1800), under the title of *Love*.—ED.

O LEAVE the lily on its stem ;
   O leave the rose upon the spray ;
O leave the elder-bloom, fair maids !
      And listen to my lay.

A cypress and a myrtle bough
This morn around my harp you twined,
Because it fashion'd mournfully
      Its murmurs in the wind.

And now a tale of love and woe,
A woeful tale of love I sing ;
Hark, gentle maidens ! hark, it sighs
      And trembles on the string.

But most, my own dear Genevieve,
It sighs and trembles most for thee !
O come and hear the cruel wrongs,
      Befell the Dark Ladie !

Few sorrows hath she of her own,
My hope, my joy, my Genevieve !
She loves me best whene'er I sing
      The songs that make her grieve.

All thoughts, all passions, all delights,
Whatever stirs this mortal frame,
All are but ministers of Love,
      And feed his sacred flame.

Oft in my waking dreams do I
Live o'er again that happy hour,
When midway on the mount I lay,*
    Beside the ruin'd tower.

The moonshine stealing o'er the scene
Had blended with the lights of eve ;
And she was there, my hope, my joy,
    My own dear Genevieve !

She lean'd against the armed man,
The statue of the armed knight ;
She stood and listen'd to my lay,†
    Amid the lingering light.

I play'd a soft and doleful air,‡
I sang an old and moving story—
An old rude song, that suited well §
    That ruin wild and hoary.

She listen'd with a flitting blush,
With downcast eyes and modest grace ;
For well she knew I could not choose
    But gaze upon her face.

  * O ever in my waking dreams
     I dwell upon that happy hour
   When midway on the Mount I sate—1799.

  † To my harp—*ib.*

  ‡ A sad and doleful air—*ib.*

  § That fitted well—*ib.*

I told her of the Knight that wore
Upon his shield a burning brand ;
And how for ten long years he woo'd
    The Ladie of the Land.

I told her how he pined : and ah !
The deep, the low, the pleading tone *
With which I sang another's love,
    Interpreted my own.

She listen'd with a flitting blush,
With downcast eyes and modest grace ;
And she forgave me that I gazed
    Too fondly on her face !

But when I told the cruel scorn
That crazed that bold and lovely Knight,
And how he roam'd the mountain-woods,
    Nor rested day nor night ;

[And how he cross'd the woodman's paths,
Through briars and swampy mosses beat ;
How boughs rebounding scourged his limbs
    And low stubs gored his feet ;]

How sometimes from the savage den,
And sometimes from the darksome shade,
And sometimes starting up at once
    In green and sunny glade,—

* The low, the deep, the pleading tone—1799.

There came and look'd him in the face
An angel beautiful and bright;
And how he knew it was a Fiend,
 This miserable Knight !

And how, unknowing what he did,
He leap'd amid a murderous band,*
And saved from outrage worse than death
 The Ladie of the Land ;—

And how she wept and clasp'd his knees ;
And how she tended him in vain—
And ever strove † to expiate
 The scorn that crazed his brain ;—

And how she nursed him in a cave ;
And how his madness went away
When on the yellow forest-leaves
 A dying man he lay ;—

His dying words—but when I reach'd
That tenderest strain of all the ditty,
My faltering voice and pausing harp
 Disturb'd her soul with pity !

All impulses of soul and sense
Had thrill'd my guileless Genevieve ;
The music and the doleful tale,
 The rich and balmy eve ;

* A lawless band—1799.   † Meekly strove—*ib.*

And hopes, and fears that kindle hope,
An undistinguishable throng,
And gentle wishes long subdued,
  Subdued and cherish'd long !

She wept with pity and delight,
She blush'd with love and virgin shame ; *
And, like the murmur of a dream,
  I heard her breathe my name.

Her bosom heaved—she stepp'd aside,†
As conscious of my look she stept—
Then suddenly, with timorous eye,
  She fled ‡ to me and wept.

She half inclosed me with her arms,
She press'd me with a meek embrace ;
And bending back her head, look'd up,
  And gazed upon my face.

'Twas partly love, and partly fear,
And partly 'twas a bashful art,
That I might rather feel than see
  The swelling of her heart.

 * Maiden shame ;—1799.
 † I saw her bosom heave and swell,
  Heave and swell with inward sighs—
  I could not choose but love to see
   Her gentle bosom rise.
  Her wet cheek glow'd ; she stept aside, &c.—*ib*.
 ‡ Flew—*ib*.

I calm'd her fears, and she was calm,
  And told her love with virgin pride;
And so I won my Genevieve,
    My bright and beauteous Bride!

And now once more a tale of woe,
  A woeful tale of love I sing;
For thee, my Genevieve, it sighs,
    And trembles on the string.

When last I sang the cruel scorn
  That crazed this bold and lovely knight,
And how he roam'd the mountain woods,
    Nor rested day nor night;

I promised thee a sister tale
  Of man's perfidious cruelty;
Come then and hear what cruel wrong
    Befell the Dark Ladie.

END OF THE INTRODUCTION.

## THE BALLAD OF THE DARK LADIE.

### A FRAGMENT.

BENEATH yon birch with silver bark
  And boughs so pendulous and fair,
The brook falls scatter'd down the rock:
  And all is mossy there!

VOL. II.        H

And there upon the moss she sits,
The Dark Ladie in silent pain ;
The heavy tear is in her eye,
    And drops and swells again.

Three times she sends her little page
Up the castled mountain's breast,
If he might find the Knight that wears
    The Griffin for his crest.

The sun was sloping down the sky,
And she had linger'd there all day,
Counting moments, dreaming fears—
    O wherefore can he stay?

She hears a rustling o'er the brook,
She sees far off a swinging bough !
" 'Tis He !  'Tis my betrothed Knight !
    Lord Falkland, it is Thou !"

She springs, she clasps him round the neck,
She sobs a thousand hopes and fears,
Her kisses glowing on his cheeks
    She quenches with her tears.

    *      *      *      *      *      *

" My friends with rude ungentle words
They scoff and bid me fly to thee !
O give me shelter in thy breast !
    O shield and shelter me !

" My Henry, I have given thee much,
I gave what I can ne'er recall,
I gave my heart, I gave my peace,
    O Heaven ! I gave thee all."

The Knight made answer to the Maid,
While to his heart he held her hand,
" Nine castles hath my noble sire,
    None statelier in the land.

" The fairest one shall be my love's,
The fairest castle of the nine !
Wait only till the stars peep out,
    The fairest shall be thine :

" Wait only till the hand of eve
Hath wholly closed yon western bars,
And through the dark we two will steal
    Beneath the twinkling stars !"—

" The dark ? the dark ?  No ! not the dark ?
The twinkling stars ?  How, Henry ?  How ?
O God ! 'twas in the eye of noon
    He pledged his sacred vow !

" And in the eye of noon my love
Shall lead me from my mother's door,
Sweet boys and girls all clothed in white
    Strewing flowers before :

" But first the nodding minstrels go
With music meet for lordly bowers,

The children next in snow-white vests,
    Strewing buds and flowers !

" And then my love and I shall pace,
My jet black hair in pearly braids,
Between our comely bachelors
    And blushing bridal maids."

\*       \*       \*       \*       \*       \*

## LEWTI,

### OR THE CIRCASSIAN'S LOVE-CHANT. \*

AT midnight by the stream I roved,
    To forget the form I loved.
Image of Lewti ! from my mind
Depart ; for Lewti is not kind.

The Moon was high, the moonlight gleam
    And the shadow of a star
Heaved upon Tamaha's stream ;
    But the rock shone brighter far,
The rock half shelter'd from my view
By pendent boughs of tressy yew.—
So shines my Lewti's forehead fair,
Gleaming through her sable hair.
Image of Lewti ! from my mind
Depart ; for Lewti is not kind.

\* *Morning Post*, April 13, 1798.

[I saw the white waves, o'er and o'er,
Break against the distant shore.
All at once upon the sight,
All at once they broke in light :
I heard no murmur of their roar,
Nor ever I beheld them flowing,
Neither coming, neither going ;
But only saw them, o'er and o'er,
Break against the curved shore ;
Now disappearing from the sight,
Now twinkling regular and white ;
And Lewti's smiling mouth can show
As white and regular a row.
Nay, treacherous image ! from my mind
Depart ; for Lewti is not kind.]

I saw a cloud of palest hue,
    Onward to the moon it pass'd ;
Still brighter and more bright it grew,
With floating colours not a few,
    Till it reach'd the moon at last :
Then the cloud was wholly bright
With a rich and amber light !
And so with many a hope I seek
    And with such joy I find my Lewti ;
And even so my pale wan cheek
    Drinks in as deep a flush of beauty !
Nay, treacherous image ! leave my mind,
If Lewti never will be kind.

The little cloud—it floats away,
    Away it goes ; away so soon ?

Alas ! it has no power to stay :
Its hues are dim, its hues are grey—
   Away it passes from the moon !
How mournfully it seems to fly,
   Ever fading more and more,
To joyless regions of the sky—
   And now 'tis whiter than before !
As white as my poor cheek will be,
   When, Lewti ! on my couch I lie,
A dying man for love of thee.
Nay, treacherous image ! leave my mind—
And yet, thou didst not look unkind.

   I saw a vapour in the sky,
   Thin, and white, and very high ;
I ne'er beheld so thin a cloud :
   Perhaps the breezes that can fly
   Now below and now above,
Have snatch'd aloft the lawny shroud
   Of lady fair—that died for love.
For maids, as well as youths, have perish'd
From fruitless love too fondly cherish'd.
Nay, treacherous image ! leave my mind—
Though Lewti never will be kind,
[This hand should make his life-blood flow
That ever scorn'd my Lewti so !

I cannot choose but fix my sight
On that small vapour, thin and white !
So thin, it scarcely, I protest,
   Bedims the star that shines behind it ;

And pity dwells in Lewti's breast,
　　Alas ! if I knew how to find it.
And O ! how sweet it were, I wist,
　　To see my Lewti's eyes to-morrow
Shine brightly through as thin a mist
　　Of pity and repentant sorrow !
Nay, treacherous image ! leave my mind—
Ah, Lewti ! why art thou unkind ?]

Hush ! my heedless feet from under
　　Slip the crumbling banks for ever :
Like echoes to a distant thunder,
　　They plunge into the gentle river.
The river-swans have heard my tread,
And startle from their reedy bed.
O beauteous birds ! methinks ye measure
　　Your movements to some heavenly tune !
O beauteous birds ! 'tis such a pleasure
　　To see you move beneath the moon,
I would it were your true delight
To sleep by day and wake all night.

I know the place where Lewti lies
When silent night has closed her eyes :
　　It is a breezy jasmine-bower,
The nightingale sings o'er her head :
　　Voice of the night ! had I the power
That leafy labyrinth to thread,
And creep, like thee, with soundless tread,
I then might view her bosom white

Heaving lovely to my sight,*
As these two swans together heave
On the gently-swelling wave.

Oh! that she saw me in a dream,
    And dreamt that I had died for care;
All pale and wasted I would seem
    Yet fair withal, as spirits are!
I'd die indeed, if I might see
Her bosom heave, and heave for me!
Soothe, gentle image! soothe my mind!
To-morrow Lewti may be kind.


## THE PICTURE,

### OR THE LOVER'S RESOLUTION.†

THROUGH weeds and thorns, and matted
        underwood,
I force my way; now climb, and now descend
O'er rocks, or bare or mossy, with wild‡ foot

---

* Had I the enviable power
        To creep unseen with noiseless tread
    Then should I view her bosom white
    Heaving lovely to the sight—1798.

This passage was altered at the suggestion of Charles Lamb, who wrote to Coleridge :—"The epithet *enviable* would damn the finest poem."

† *Morning Post*, September 6, 1802.

‡ With blind foot—1802.

Crushing the purple whorts;\* while oft unseen,
Hurrying along the drifted forest-leaves,
The scared snake rustles.  Onward still I toil,
I know not, ask not whither !  A new joy,
Lovely as light, sudden as summer gust,
And gladsome as the first-born of the spring,
Beckons me on, or follows from behind,
Playmate, or guide ! The master-passion quell'd,
I feel that I am free.  With dun-red bark
The fir-trees, and the unfrequent slender oak,
Forth from this tangle wild of bush and brake
Soar up, and form a melancholy vault
High o'er me, murmuring like a distant sea.

Here Wisdom might resort, and here Remorse ;
Here too the love-lorn man, who, sick in soul,
And of this busy human heart aweary,
Worships the spirit of unconscious life
In tree or wild-flower.—Gentle lunatic !
If so he might not wholly cease to be,
He would far rather not be that he is ;
But would be something that he knows not of,
In winds or waters, or among the rocks !

   But hence, fond wretch ! breathe not contagion
      here !
No myrtle-walks are these : these are no groves

---

\* *Vaccinium Myrtillus*, known by the different names of
Whorts, Whortle-berries, Bilberries; and in the North of
England, Blea-berries and Bloom-berries.
                                    [Note by S. T. C. 1802.]

Where Love dare loiter !   If in sullen mood
He should stray hither, the low stumps shall gore
His dainty feet, the brier and the thorn
Make his plumes haggard.   Like a wounded bird
Easily caught, ensnare him, O ye Nymphs,
Ye Oreads chaste, ye dusky Dryades !
And you, ye Earth-winds ! you that make at morn
The dew-drops quiver on the spiders' webs !
You, O ye wingless Airs ! that creep between
The rigid stems of heath and bitten furze,
Within whose scanty shade, at summer-noon,
The mother-sheep hath worn a hollow bed—
Ye, that now cool her fleece with dropless damp,
Now pant and murmur with her feeding lamb.
Chase, chase him, all ye Fays, and elfin Gnomes !
With prickles sharper than his darts bemock
His little Godship, making him perforce
Creep through a thorn-bush on yon hedgehog's back.

This is my hour of triumph !   I can now
With my own fancies play the merry fool,
And laugh away worse folly, being free.
Here will I seat myself, beside this old,
Hollow, and weedy oak, which ivy-twine
Clothes as with net-work : here will couch my
      limbs,
Close by this river, in this silent shade,
As safe and sacred from the step of man
As an invisible world—unheard, unseen,
And listening only to the pebbly brook
That murmurs with a dead, yet tinkling sound ;

Or to the bees,\* that in the neighbouring trunk
Make honey-hoards.   The breeze that visits me
Was never Love's accomplice, never raised
The tendril ringlets from the maiden's brow,
And the blue delicate veins above her cheek ;
Ne'er play'd the wanton—never half disclosed
The maiden's snowy bosom, scattering thence
Eye-poisons for some love-distemper'd youth,
Who ne'er henceforth may see an aspen-grove
Shiver in sunshine, but his feeble heart
Shall flow away like a dissolving thing.

Sweet breeze ! thou only, if I guess aright,
Liftest the feathers of the robin's breast,
That swells its little breast,† so full of song,
Singing above me, on the mountain-ash.
And thou too, desert stream ! no pool of thine,
Though clear as lake in latest summer-eve,
Did e'er reflect the stately virgin's robe,
The face, the form divine, the downcast look
Contemplative !   Behold ! her open palm
Presses her cheek and brow ! her elbow rests ‡
On the bare branch of half-uprooted tree,
That leans towards its mirror !   Who erewhile

---

\* And listening only to the pebbly stream
  That murmurs with a dead yet bell-like sound
  Tinkling, or bees, &c.—1802.

† Who swells his little breast—*Ib.*

‡       Her downcast look
  Contemplative, her cheek upon her palm
  Supported ; the white arm and elbow rest, &c.—*ib.*

Had from her countenance turn'd, or look'd by
    stealth,
(For fear is true-love's cruel nurse), he now
With steadfast gaze and unoffending eye,
Worships the watery idol, dreaming hopes
Delicious to the soul, but fleeting, vain,
E'en as that phantom-world on which he gazed,
But not unheeded gazed : for see, ah ! see,
The sportive tyrant with her left hand plucks
The heads of tall flowers that behind her grow,
Lychnis, and willow-herb, and fox-glove bells :
And suddenly, as one that toys with time,
Scatters them on the pool !   Then all the charm
Is broken—all that phantom world so fair
Vanishes, and a thousand circlets spread,
And each mis-shape the other.   Stay awhile,
Poor youth, who scarcely darest lift up thine eyes—
The stream will soon renew its smoothness, soon
The visions will return !   And lo ! he stays :
And soon the fragments dim of lovely forms
Come trembling back, unite, and now once more
The pool becomes a mirror ; and behold
Each wild-flower on the marge inverted there,
And there the half-uprooted tree—but where,
O where the virgin's snowy arm, that lean'd
On its bare branch ?   He turns, and she is gone !
Homeward she steals through many a woodland
    maze
Which he shall seek in vain.   Ill-fated youth !
Go, day by day, and waste thy manly prime
In mad love-yearning by the vacant brook,

Till sickly thoughts bewitch thine eyes, and thou
Behold'st her shadow still abiding there,
The Naiad of the mirror !

                Not to thee,
O wild and desert stream ! belongs this tale :
Gloomy and dark art thou—the crowded firs
Spire from thy shores,* and stretch across thy bed,
Making thee doleful as a cavern-well :
Save when the shy king-fishers build their nest
On thy steep banks, no loves hast thou, wild
     stream !

  This be my chosen haunt—emancipate
From passion's dreams, a freeman, and alone,
I rise and trace its devious course.   O lead,
Lead me to deeper shades and lonelier glooms.
Lo ! stealing through the canopy of firs,
How fair the sunshine spots that mossy rock,
Isle of the river, whose disparted waves
Dart off asunder with an angry sound,
How soon to re-unite !   And see ! they meet,
Each in the other lost and found : and see
Placeless, as spirits, one soft water-sun
Throbbing within them, heart at once and eye !
With its soft neighbourhood of filmy clouds,
The stains and shadings of forgotten tears,
Dimness o'erswum with lustre !   Such the hour

---

\* Tower from thy shores—1802.

Of deep enjoyment, following love's brief feuds ; *
And hark, the noise of a near waterfall !
I pass forth into light †—I find myself
Beneath a weeping birch (most beautiful
Of forest trees, the lady of the woods),
Hard by the brink of a tall weedy rock
That overbrows the cataract.   How bursts
The landscape on my sight !   Two crescent hills
Fold in behind each other, and so make
A circular vale, and land-lock'd, as might seem,
With brook and bridge, and grey stone cottages,
Half hid by rocks and fruit-trees.   At my feet,
The whortle-berries are bedew'd with spray,
Dash'd upwards by the furious waterfall.
How solemnly the pendent ivy-mass
Swings in its winnow !   All the air is calm.
The smoke from cottage-chimneys, tinged with light,
Rises in columns ; from this house alone,
Close by the waterfall, the column slants,
And feels its ceaseless breeze.   But what is this ?
That cottage, with its slanting chimney-smoke,
And close beside its porch a sleeping child,
His dear head pillow'd on a sleeping dog—
One arm between its fore-legs, and the hand
Holds loosely its small handful of wild-flowers,

---

* How soon to reunite !   They meet, they join
  In deep embrace, and open to the sun
  Lie calm and smooth.   Such the delicious hour
  Of deep enjoyment, following love's brief quarrels !

                                              1802.

† I come out into light—*Ib.*

Unfilleted, and of unequal lengths.
A curious picture, with a master's haste
Sketch'd on a strip of pinky-silver skin,
Peel'd from the birchen bark! Divinest maid!
Yon bark her canvas, and those purple berries
Her pencil! See, the juice is scarcely dried
On the fine skin! She has been newly here;
And lo! yon patch of heath has been her couch—
The pressure still remains! O blessed couch!
For this may'st thou flower early, and the sun,
Slanting at eve, rest bright, and linger long
Upon thy purple bells! O Isabel!
Daughter of genius! stateliest of our maids!
More beautiful than whom Alcæus woo'd,
The Lesbian woman of immortal song!
O child of genius! stately, beautiful,
And full of love to all, save only me,
And not ungentle even to me! My heart,
Why beats it thus? Through yonder coppice-wood
Needs must the pathway turn, that leads straight-
        way*
On to her father's house. She is alone!
The night draws on—such ways are hard to hit—
And fit it is I should restore this sketch,
Dropt unawares no doubt. Why should I yearn
To keep the relique? 'twill but idly feed
The passion that consumes me. Let me haste!
The picture in my hand which she has left;
She cannot blame me that I follow'd her:
And I may be her guide the long wood through.

* That leads away—1802.

# FIRE, FAMINE, AND SLAUGHTER.

## A WAR ECLOGUE.

## APOLOGETIC PREFACE.

AT the house of a gentleman * who by the principles and corresponding virtues of a sincere Christian consecrates a cultivated genius and the favourable accidents of birth, opulence, and splendid connexions, it was my good fortune to meet, in a dinner-party, with more men of celebrity in science or polite literature than are commonly found collected round the same table. In the course of conversation, one of the party reminded an illustrious poet, then present, of some verses which he had recited that morning, and which had appeared in a newspaper under the name of a War-Eclogue, in which Fire, Famine, and Slaughter were introduced as the speakers. The gentleman so addressed replied, that he was rather surprised that none of us should have noticed or heard of the poem, as it had been at the time a good deal talked of in Scotland. It may be easily supposed that my feelings were at this moment not of the most comfortable kind. Of all present, one only knew, or suspected me to be the author; a man who would have established himself in the first rank of England's living poets, if the Genius of our country had not decreed that he should rather be the first in the first rank of its philosophers and scientific benefactors. It appeared the general wish to hear the lines. As my friend chose to remain silent, I chose to follow his example, and Mr. ***** recited the poem. This he could do with the better grace, being known to have ever been not only a firm and

* According to De Quincey, this party took place at the house of Mr. Sotheby. It was Mr., afterwards Sir Walter Scott, who recited the poem. § *Coleridge and Opium-Eating*, De Quincey's Works, XI. 86.—ED.

active Anti-Jacobin and Anti-Gallican, but likewise a zealous admirer of Mr. Pitt, both as a good man and a great statesman. As a poet exclusively, he had been amused with the Eclogue; as a poet he recited it; and in a spirit which made it evident that he would have read and repeated it with the same pleasure had his own name been attached to the imaginary object or agent.

After the recitation our amiable host observed that in his opinion Mr. ***** had over-rated the merits of the poetry; but had they been tenfold greater, they could not have compensated for that malignity of heart which could alone have prompted sentiments so atrocious. I perceived that my illustrious friend became greatly distressed on my account; but fortunately I was able to preserve fortitude and presence of mind enough to take up the subject without exciting even a suspicion how nearly and painfully it interested me.

What follows is the substance of what I then replied,* but dilated and in language less colloquial. It was not my intention, I said, to justify the publication, whatever its author's feelings might have been at the time of composing it. That they are calculated to call forth so severe a reprobation from a good man, is not the worst feature of such poems. Their moral deformity is aggravated in proportion to the pleasure which they are capable of affording to vindictive, turbulent, and unprincipled readers. Could it be supposed, though for a moment, that the author seriously wished what he had thus wildly imagined, even the attempt to palliate an inhumanity so monstrous would be an insult to the hearers. But it seemed to me

* is substantially the same as I then replied—1817.

worthy of consideration, whether the mood of mind and the general state of sensations in which a poet produces such vivid and fantastic images, is likely to co-exist, or is even compatible, with that gloomy and deliberate ferocity which a serious wish to realize them would pre-suppose. It had been often observed, and all my experience tended to confirm the observation, that prospects of pain and evil to others, and in general all deep feelings of revenge, are commonly expressed in a few words, ironically tame, and mild. The mind under so direful and fiend-like an influence seems to take a morbid pleasure in contrasting the intensity of its wishes and feelings with the slightness or levity of the expressions by which they are hinted; and indeed feelings so intense and solitary, if they were not precluded (as in almost all cases they would be) by a constitutional activity of fancy and association, and by the specific joyousness combined with it, would assuredly themselves preclude such activity. Passion, in its own quality, is the antagonist of action; though in an ordinary and natural degree the former alternates with the latter, and thereby revives and strengthens it. But the more intense and insane the passion is, the fewer and the more fixed are the correspondent forms and notions. A rooted hatred, an inveterate thirst of revenge, is a sort of madness, and still eddies round its favourite object, and exercises as it were a perpetual tautology of mind in thoughts and words which admit of no adequate substitutes. Like a fish in a globe of glass, it moves restlessly round and round the scanty circumference, which it cannot leave without losing its vital element.

There is a second character of such imaginary representations as spring from a real and earnest desire of evil to another, which we often see in real life, and might even anticipate from the nature of the mind. The images, I mean, that a vindictive man places before his imagination, will most often be taken from the realities of life : they will be images of pain and suffering which he has himself seen inflicted on other men, and which he can fancy himself as inflicting on the object of his hatred. I will suppose that we had heard at different times two common sailors, each speaking of some one who had wronged or offended him : that the first with apparent violence had devoted every part of his adversary's body and soul to all the horrid phantoms and fantastic places that ever Quevedo dreamt of, and this in a rapid flow of those outrageous * and wildly combined execrations, which too often with our lower classes serve for escape-valves to carry off the excess of their passions, as so much superfluous steam that would endanger the vessel if it were retained. The other, on the contrary, with that sort of calmness of tone which is to the ear what the paleness of anger is to the eye, shall simply say, " If I chance to be made boatswain, as I hope I soon shall, and can but once get that fellow under my hand (and I shall be upon the watch for him), I'll tickle his pretty skin ! I won't hurt him ! oh no ! I'll only cut the —— to the liver !" I dare appeal to all present, which of the two they would regard as the least deceptive symptom of deliberate malignity ? nay, whether it would surprise them to see the first fellow, an hour or two afterwards, cordially shaking hands with the very man the fractional parts of whose body and soul he had been so charitably disposing of ; or even perhaps risking his life for him ? What language Shakespeare considered characteristic of malignant disposition we see

* *Outré*—1817.

in the speech of the good-natured Gratiano, who spoke
" an infinite deal of nothing more than any man in all
Venice ;"

———" Too wild, too rude and bold of voice !"

the skipping spirit, whose thoughts and words recipro-
cally ran away with each other ;

———" O be thou damn'd, inexorable dog !
And for thy life let justice be accused !"

and the wild fancies that follow, contrasted with Shy-
lock's tranquil " I stand here for Law."

Or, to take a case more analogous to the present
subject, should we hold it either fair or charitable to
believe it to have been Dante's serious wish that all
the persons mentioned by him (many recently departed, and some even alive at the time,) should actually suffer the fantastic and horrible punishments to
which he has sentenced them in his Hell and Purgatory ?   Or what shall we say of the passages in which
Bishop Jeremy Taylor anticipates the state of those
who, vicious themselves, have been the cause of vice
and misery to their fellow-creatures ?   Could we endure for a moment to think that a spirit, like Bishop
Taylor's, burning with Christian love ; that a man
constitutionally overflowing with pleasurable kindli-
ness ; who scarcely even in a casual illustration intro-
duces the image of woman, child, or bird, but he em-
balms the thought with so rich a tenderness, as makes
the very words seem beauties and fragments of poetry
from [a] Euripides or Simonides ;—can we endure to
think, that a man so natured and so disciplined, did at
the time of composing this horrible picture, attach a sober feeling of reality to the phrases ? or that he would
have described in the same tone of justification, in the

same luxuriant flow of phrases, the tortures about to
be inflicted on a living individual by a verdict of the
Star-Chamber? or the still more atrocious sentences
executed on the Scotch anti-prelatists and schismatics,
at the command, and in some instances under the
very eye of the Duke of Lauderdale, and of that
wretched bigot who afterwards dishonoured and for-
feited the throne of Great Britain? Or do we not
rather feel and understand, that these violent words
were mere bubbles, flashes and electrical apparitions,
from the magic cauldron of a fervid and ebullient
fancy, constantly fuelled by an unexampled opulence
of language?

Were I now to have read by myself for the first
time the poem in question, my conclusion, I fully believe, would be, that the writer must have been some
man of warm feelings and active fancy; that he had
painted to himself the circumstances that accompany
war in so many vivid and yet fantastic forms, as
proved that neither the images nor the feelings were
the result of observation, or in any way derived from
realities. I should judge that they were the product
of his own seething imagination, and therefore im-
pregnated with that pleasurable exultation which is
experienced in all energetic exertion of intellectual
power; that in the same mood he had generalized the
causes of the war, and then personified the abstract
and christened it by the name which he had been
accustomed to hear most often associated with its
management and measures. I should guess that the
minister was in the author's mind at the moment of
composition, as completely ἀπαθὴς, ἀναιμόσαρκος, as
Anacreon's grasshopper, and that he had as little
notion of a real person of flesh and blood,

" Distinguishable in member, joint, or limb,"

as Milton had in the grim and terrible phantoms (half person, half allegory) which he has placed at the gates of Hell. I concluded by observing, that the poem was not calculated to excite passion in any mind, or to make any impression except on poetic readers; and that from the culpable levity betrayed at the close of the eclogue by the grotesque union of epigrammatic wit with allegoric personification, in the allusion to the most fearful of thoughts, I should conjecture that the "rantin' Bardie," instead of really believing, much less wishing, the fate spoken of in the last line, in application to any human individual, would shrink from passing the verdict even on the Devil himself, and exclaim with poor Burns,

> But fare ye weel, auld Nickie-ben !
> Oh ! wad ye tak a thought an' men !
> Ye aiblins might—I dinna ken—
>      Still hae a stake—
> I'm wae to think upon yon den,
>      Ev'n for your sake !

I need not say that these thoughts, which are here dilated, were in such a company only rapidly suggested. Our kind host smiled, and with a courteous compliment observed, that the defence was too good for the cause. My voice faltered a little, for I was somewhat agitated; though not so much on my own account as for the uneasiness that so kind and friendly a man would feel from the thought that he had been the occasion of distressing me. At length I brought out these words : "I must now confess, sir ! that I am the author of that poem. It was written some years ago. I do not attempt to justify my past self, young as I then was; but as little as I would now write a similar poem, so far was I even then from imagining that the lines would be taken as more or less than a sport of fancy. At all events, if I know my own heart, there was never a moment in my existence in which I should have been more ready, had Mr. Pitt's person been in hazard, to interpose my own body, and defend his life at the risk of my own."

I have prefaced the poem with this anecdote, because to have printed it without any remark might well have been understood as implying an unconditional approbation on my part, and this after many years' consideration. But if it be asked why I re-published it at all, I answer, that the poem had been attributed at different times to different other persons; and what I had dared beget, I thought it neither manly nor honourable not to dare father. From the same motives I should have published perfect copies of two poems, the one entitled *The Devil's Thoughts*, and the other, *The Two Round Spaces on the Tombstone*,* but that the first three stanzas of the former, which were worth all the rest of the poem, and the best stanza of the remainder, were written by a friend of deserved celebrity; and because there are passages in both which might have given offence to the religious feelings of certain readers. I myself indeed see no reason why vulgar superstitions and absurd conceptions that deform the pure faith of a Christian should possess a greater immunity from ridicule than stories of witches, or the fables of Greece and Rome. But

---

* These two pieces Coleridge was afterwards induced to republish, a portion of the former appearing in the collected edition of his Poems published in 1829, and perfect copies of both in the edition of 1834. The "friend of deserved celebrity" mentioned as the joint author of *The Devil's Thoughts* was Robert Southey.—ED.

there are those who deem it profaneness and irreve-
rence to call an ape an ape, if it but wear a monk's
cowl on its head; and I would rather reason with
this weakness than offend it.

The passage from Jeremy Taylor to which I referred
is found in his second Sermon on Christ's Advent to
Judgment; which is likewise the second in his year's
course of sermons. Among many remarkable passages
of the same character in those discourses, I have
selected this as the most so. " But when this Lion of
the tribe of Judah shall appear, then Justice shall
strike, and Mercy shall not hold her hands; she shall
strike sore strokes, and Pity shall not break the blow.
As there are treasures of good things, so hath God a
treasure of wrath and fury, and scourges and scorpions;
and then shall be produced the shame of Lust and the
malice of Envy, and the groans of the oppressed and
the persecutions of the saints, and the cares of Covet-
ousness and the troubles of Ambition, and the insolen-
cies of traitors and the violences of rebels, and the rage
of anger and the uneasiness of impatience, and the restlessness of unlawful desires; and by this time the
monsters and diseases will be numerous and intolerable, when God's heavy hand shall press the *sanies*
and the intolerableness, the obliquity and the unreason-
ableness, the amazement and the disorder, the smart
and the sorrow, the guilt and the punishment, out from
all our sins, and pour them into one chalice, and
mingle them with an infinite wrath, and make the
wicked drink off all the vengeance, and force it down
their unwilling throats with the violence of devils and
accursed spirits."

That this Tartarean drench displays the imagination
rather than the discretion of the compounder; that, in
short, this passage and others of the same kind are in a

bad taste, few will deny at the present day. It would, doubtless, have more behoved the good bishop not to be wise beyond what is written on a subject in which Eternity is opposed to Time, and a Death threatened, not the negative, but the positive opposite of Life; a subject, therefore, which must of necessity be indescribable to the human understanding in our present state. But I can neither find nor believe that it ever occurred to any reader to ground on such passages a charge against Bishop Taylor's humanity, or goodness of heart. I was not a little surprised therefore to find, in the " Pursuits of Literature " and other works, so horrible a sentence passed on Milton's moral character, for a passage in his prose writings, as nearly parallel to this of Taylor's as two passages can well be conceived to be. All his merits, as a poet, forsooth—all the glory of having written the " Paradise Lost," are light in the scale, nay, kick the beam, compared with the atrocious malignity of heart, expressed in the offensive paragraph. I remembered, in general, that Milton had concluded one of his works on Reformation, written in the fervour of his youthful imagination, in a high poetic strain, that wanted metre only to become a lyrical poem. I remembered that in the former part he had formed to himself a perfect ideal of human virtue, a character of heroic, disinterested zeal and devotion for Truth, Religion, and public Liberty, in act and in suffering, in the day of triumph and in the hour of martyrdom. Such spirits, as more excellent than others, he describes as having a more excellent reward, and as distinguished by a transcendent glory: and this reward and this glory he displays and particularizes with an energy and brilliance that announced the Paradise Lost as plainly, as ever the bright purple clouds in the east announced the coming of the Sun.

Milton then passes to the gloomy contrast, to such men as from motives of selfish ambition and the lust of personal aggrandizement should, against their own light, persecute truth and the true religion, and wilfully abuse the powers and gifts entrusted to them, to bring vice, blindness, misery and slavery, on their native country, on the very country that had trusted, enriched and honoured them. Such beings, after that speedy and appropriate removal from their sphere of mischief which all good and humane men must of course desire, will, he takes for granted by parity of reason, meet with a punishment, an ignominy, and a retaliation, as much severer than other wicked men, as their guilt and its consequences were more enormous. His description of this imaginary punishment presents more distinct pictures to the fancy than the extract from Jeremy Taylor; but the thoughts in the latter are incomparably more exaggerated and horrific. All this I knew; but I neither remembered, nor by reference and careful re-perusal could discover, any other meaning, either in Milton or Taylor, but that good men will be rewarded, and the impenitent wicked punished, in proportion to their dispositions and intentional acts in this life; and that if the punishment of the least wicked be fearful beyond conception, all words and descriptions must be so far true, that they must fall short of the punishment that awaits the transcendently wicked. Had Milton stated either his ideal of virtue, or of depravity, as an individual or individuals actually existing? Certainly not. Is this representation worded historically, or only hypothetically? Assuredly the latter. Does he express it as his own wish that after death they should suffer these tortures? or as a general consequence, deduced from reason and revelation, that such will be their fate?

Again, the latter only. His wish is expressly confined
to a speedy stop being put by Providence to their
power of inflicting misery on others. But did he name
or refer to any persons living or dead? No. But the
calumniators of Milton dare say (for what will calumny
not dare say?) that he had Laud and Strafford in his
mind, while writing of remorseless persecution, and
the enslavement of a free country from motives of
selfish ambition. Now what if a stern anti-prela-
tist should dare say, that in speaking of the "insolen-
cies of traitors and the violences of rebels," Bishop
Taylor must have individualised in his mind Hamp-
den, Hollis, Pym, Fairfax, Ireton, and Milton? And
what if he should take the liberty of concluding, that,
in the after-description, the Bishop was feeding and
feasting his party-hatred, and with those individuals
before the eyes of his imagination enjoying, trait by
trait, horror after horror, the picture of their intolerable agonies? Yet this bigot would have an equal
right thus to criminate the one good and great man,
as these men have to criminate the other. Milton
has said, and I doubt not but that Taylor with equal
truth could have said it, "that in his whole life he
never spake against a man even that his skin should
be grazed." He asserted this when one of his opponents (either Bishop Hall or his nephew) had called
upon the women and children in the streets to take up
stones and stone him (Milton). It is known that
Milton repeatedly used his interest to protect the
royalists; but even at a time when all lies would have
been meritorious against him, no charge was made,
no story pretended, that he had ever directly or
indirectly engaged or assisted in their persecution.
Oh! methinks there are other and far better feelings
which should be acquired by the perusal of our great

elder writers. When I have before me, on the same table, the works of Hammond and Baxter; when I reflect with what joy and dearness their blessed spirits are now loving each other; it seems a mournful thing that their names should be perverted to an occasion of bitterness among us, who are enjoying that happy mean which the human too-much on both sides was perhaps necessary to produce. "The tangle of delusions which stifled and distorted the growing tree of our well-being has been torn away; the parasite-weeds that fed on its very roots have been plucked up with a salutary violence. To us there remain only quiet duties, the constant care, the gradual improvement, the cautious unhazardous labours of the industrious though contented gardener—to prune, to strengthen, to engraft, and one by one to remove from its leaves and fresh shoots the slug and the caterpillar. But far be it from us to undervalue with light and senseless detraction the conscientious hardihood of our predecessors, or even to condemn in them that vehemence, to which the blessings it won for us leave us now neither temptation nor pretext. We antedate the feelings, in order to criminate the authors, of our present liberty, light and toleration." *

If ever two great men might seem, during their whole lives, to have moved in direct opposition, though neither of them has at any time introduced the name of the other, Milton and Jeremy Taylor were they. The former commenced his career by attacking the Church-Liturgy and all set forms of prayer. The latter, but far more successfully, by defending both. Milton's next work was against the Prelacy and the then existing Church-Government — Taylor's in

* *The Friend*, p. 54.

vindication and support of them. Milton became more and more a stern republican, or rather an advocate for that religious and moral aristrocacy which, in his day, was called republicanism, and which, even more than royalism itself, is the direct antipode of modern jacobinism. Taylor, as more and more sceptical concerning the fitness of men in general for power, became more and more attached to the prerogatives of monarchy. From Calvinism, with a still decreasing respect for Fathers, Councils, and for Church-antiquity in general, Milton seems to have ended in an indifference, if not a dislike, to all forms of ecclesiastic government, and to have retreated wholly into the inward and spiritual church-communion of his own spirit with the Light that lighteth every man that cometh into the world. Taylor, with a growing reverence for authority, an increasing sense of the insufficiency of the Scriptures without the aids of tradition and the consent of authorized interpreters, advanced as far in his approaches (not indeed to Popery, but) to Catholicism, as a conscientious minister of the English Church could well venture. Milton would be and would utter the same to all on all occasions: he would tell the truth, the whole truth, and nothing but the truth. Taylor would become all things to all men, if by any means he might benefit any; hence he availed himself, in his popular writings, of opinions and representations which stand often in striking contrast with the doubts and convictions expressed in his more philosophical works. He appears, indeed, not too severely to have blamed that management of truth *(istam falsitatem dispensativam)* authorised and exemplified by almost all the fathers: " Integrum omnino doctoribus et cœtus Christiani antistitibus esse, ut dolos versent, falsa veris intermisceant et imprimis religionis hostes fallant, dummodo veritatis commodis et utilitati inserviant."

The same antithesis might be carried on with the elements of their several intellectual powers. Milton, austere, condensed, imaginative, supporting his truth by direct enunciation of lofty moral sentiment and by distinct visual representations, and in the same spirit overwhelming what he deemed falsehood by moral denunciation and a succession of pictures appalling or repulsive. In his prose, so many metaphors, so many allegorical miniatures. Taylor, eminently discursive, accumulative, and (to use one of his own words) agglomerative; still more rich in images than Milton himself, but images of fancy, and presented to the common and passive eye, rather than to the eye of the imagination. Whether supporting or assailing, he makes his way either by argument or by appeals to the affections, unsurpassed even by the schoolmen in subtlety, agility, and logical wit, and unrivalled by the most rhetorical of the fathers in the copiousness and vividness of his expressions and illustrations. Here words that convey feelings, and words that flash images, and words of abstract notion, flow together, and whirl and rush onward like a stream, at once rapid and full of eddies; and yet still interfused here and there we see a tongue or islet of smooth water, with some picture in it of earth or sky, landscape or living group of quiet beauty.

Differing then so widely and almost contrariantly, wherein did these great men agree? wherein did they resemble each other? In genius, in learning, in unfeigned piety, in blameless purity of life, and in benevolent aspirations and purposes for the moral and temporal improvement of their fellow-creatures! Both of them wrote a Latin Accidence, to render education more easy and less painful to children; both of them composed hymns and psalms proportioned to the capacity of common congregations; both, nearly at the same time, set the glorious example of publicly recommending and supporting general toleration, and the liberty both of the pulpit and the press! In the writings of neither shall we find a single sentence, like those meek deliverances to God's mercy, with which Laud accompanied his votes for the mutilations and loathsome dungeoning of Leighton and others!—nowhere such a pious prayer as we find in Bishop Hall's memoranda of his own life, concerning the subtle and witty atheist that so grievously perplexed and gravelled him at Sir Robert Drury's till he prayed to the Lord to remove him, and behold! his prayers were heard: for shortly afterward this Philistine-combatant went to London, and there perished of the plague in great misery! In short, nowhere shall we find the least approach, in the lives and writings of John Milton or Jeremy Taylor, to that guarded gentleness, to that sighing reluctance, with which the holy brethren of the Inquisition deliver over a condemned heretic to the civil magistrate, recommending him to mercy, and hoping that the magistrate will treat the erring brother with all possible mildness!—the magistrate who too well knows what would be his own fate if he dared offend them by acting on their recommendation.

The opportunity of diverting the reader from myself to characters more worthy of his attention, has led me far beyond my first intention; but it is not unimportant to expose the false zeal which has occasioned these attacks on our elder patriots. It has been too much the fashion first to personify the Church of England, and then to speak of different individuals, who in different ages have been rulers in that church, as if in some strange way they constituted its per-

sonal identity. Why should a clergyman of the
present day feel interested in the defence of Laud or
Sheldon? Surely it is sufficient for the warmest par-
tisan of our establishment that he can assert with
truth,— when our Church persecuted, it was on mistaken principles held in common by all Christendom;
and at all events, far less culpable was this intolerance
in the Bishops, who were maintaining the existing
laws, than the persecuting spirit afterwards shown by
their successful opponents, who had no such excuse,
and who should have been taught mercy by their own
sufferings, and wisdom by the utter failure of the experiment in their own case. We can say that our
Church, apostolical in its faith, primitive in its cere-
monies, unequalled in its liturgical forms; that our
Church, which has kindled and displayed more bright
and burning lights of genius and learning than all
other protestant churches since the reformation, was
(with the single exception of the times of Laud and
Sheldon) least intolerant, when all Christians un-
happily deemed a species of intolerance their religious
duty; that Bishops of our church were among the
first that contended against this error; and finally,
that since the Reformation, when tolerance became a
fashion, the Church of England in a tolerating age,
has shown herself eminently tolerant, and far more so,
both in spirit and in fact, than many of her most bitter
opponents, who profess to deem toleration itself an
insult on the rights of mankind! As to myself, who
not only know the Church-Establishment to be
tolerant, but who see in it the greatest, if not the sole
safe bulwark of toleration, I feel no necessity of defending or palliating oppressions under the two
Charleses, in order to exclaim with a full and fervent
heart, *Esto perpetua!*

[1817.]

## FIRE, FAMINE, AND SLAUGHTER.

### A WAR ECLOGUE.*

*The Scene a desolated† Tract in La Vendée.*
FAMINE *is discovered lying‡ on the ground ;*
*to her enter* FIRE *and* SLAUGHTER.

*Fam.* SISTERS ! sisters ! who sent you here ?
*Slau.* [*to Fire*]. I will whisper it in her ear.§
*Fire.*   No ! no ! no !
Spirits hear what spirits tell :
'Twill make a holiday in Hell.
            No ! no ! no !
Myself I named him once below,
And all the souls, that damned be,
Leapt up at once in anarchy,
Clapp'd their hands and danced for glee.
They no longer heeded me ;
But laugh'd to hear Hell's burning rafters
Unwillingly re-echo laughters !
            No ! no ! no !
Spirits hear what spirits tell :
'Twill make a holiday in Hell !

* First printed in the *Morning Post*, January 8, 1798.
Reprinted in the second volume of the *Annual Anthology*,
Bristol, 1800.

   † Depopulated—1798.        ‡ Stretched—*ib.*

   § I will name him in your ear.—*Ib.*

*Fam.* Whisper it, sister ! so and so !
In a dark hint, soft and slow.*

*Slau.* Letters four do form his name—†
And who sent you?

    *Both.*           The same ! the same !

    *Slau.* He came by stealth, and unlock'd my den,
And I have drunk ‡ the blood since then
Of thrice three hundred § thousand men.

    *Both.* Who bade you do 't?

    *Slau.*           The same ! the same !
Letters four do form his name.
He let me loose, and cried Halloo !
To him alone the praise is due.

    *Fam.* Thanks, sister, thanks ! the men have bled,
Their wives and their children faint for bread.
I stood in a swampy field of battle ;
With bones and skulls I made a rattle,
To frighten the wolf and the carrion-crow
And the homeless dog—but they would not go.
So off I flew : for how could I bear
To see them gorge their dainty fare?
I heard a groan and a peevish squall,
And through the chink of a cottage-wall—
Can you guess what I saw there?

    *Both.* Whisper it, sister ! in our ear.

---

\* Then sound it not, yet let me know ;
   Darkly hint it—soft and low !—1798.

† Four letters form his name—*ib.* (And so throughout
the poem as it appeared in the *Morning Post*.)

‡ Spill'd—1798.       § Thrice ten hundred—*Ib.*

*Fam.* A baby beat its dying mother:
I had starved the one and was starving the other!
  *Both.* Who bade you do't?
  *Fam.*           The same! the same!
Letters four do form his name.
He let me loose, and cried, Halloo!
To him alone the praise is due.
  *Fire.* Sisters! I from Ireland came!
Hedge and corn-fields all on flame,
I triumph'd o'er the setting sun!
And all the while the work was done,
On as I strode with my huge strides,*
I flung back my head and I held my sides,
It was so rare a piece of fun
To see the swelter'd cattle run
With uncouth gallop through the night,†
Scared by the red and noisy light!
By the light of his own blazing cot
Was many a naked rebel shot:
The house-stream met the flame ‡ and hiss'd,
While crash! fell in the roof, I wist,
On some of those old bed-rid nurses,
That deal in discontent and curses.
  *Both.* Who bade you do't?
  *Fire.*           The same! the same!
Letters four do form his name.
He let me loose, and cried Halloo!
To him alone the praise is due.

---

  * As on I strode with monstrous strides—1798.
  † All the night—*ib.*        ‡ The fire—*ib.*

*All.* He let us loose, and cried Halloo !
How shall we yield him honour due ?
*Fam.* Wisdom comes with lack of food.
I'll gnaw, I'll gnaw the multitude,
Till the cup of rage o'erbrim :
They shall seize him and his brood—
*Slau.* They shall tear him limb from limb !
*Fire.* O thankless beldames and untrue !
And is this all that you can do
For him, who did so much for you ?
[*To Slaughter.* For *you* he turn'd the dust to mud
With his fellow-creatures' blood !
*To Famine.* And hunger scorch'd as many more
To make *your* cup of joy run o'er.
*To Both.*] Ninety months he, by my troth !
Hath richly cater'd for you both ;
And in an hour would you repay
An eight years' work ? *—Away ! away !
I alone am faithful ! I
Cling to him everlastingly.


## THE DEVIL'S THOUGHTS.†

### I.

FROM his brimstone bed at break of day
    A-walking the Devil is gone,

* An eight years' debt ?—1798.

† Printed in *The Morning Post*, Sept. 6, 1799 (with the
stanzas in a somewhat different order).

To visit his snug little farm the Earth,
  And see how his stock goes on.*

II.

Over the hill and over the dale,
  And he went over the plain,
And backward and forward he switch'd † his long
  As a gentleman switches ‡ his cane.        [tail

III.

And how then was the Devil drest?
Oh! he was in his Sunday's best:
His jacket was red and his breeches were blue,
And there was a hole where the tail came through.

IV.

He saw a Lawyer killing a viper
  On a dunghill hard by his own stable;
And the Devil smiled, for it put him in mind
  Of Cain and his brother Abel.§

V.

He saw an Apothecary on a white horse
  ‖Ride by on his vocation;

---

  * To look at his little snug farm of the earth,
      And see how his stock went on.—1799.
  † Swish'd—*Ib.*                ‡ Swishes—*Ib.*
  § On the dunghill beside his stable;
      'Oh oh,' quoth he, for it put him in mind
        Of the story of Cain and Abel.—*Ib.*
  ‖ An Apothecary on a white horse
      Rode by, &c.—*Ib.*

And the Devil thought of his old friend
   Death in the Revelation.*

### VI.

He saw a cottage with a double coach-house,
   A cottage of gentility;
And the Devil did grin, for his darling sin †
   Is pride that apes humility.

### VII.

He peep'd into a rich bookseller's shop,
   Quoth he, "We are both of one college!
For I sate myself, like a cormorant, once
   Hard by the tree ‡ of knowledge." §

---

\* And I looked, and behold a pale horse: and his name that sat on him was Death.—*Revel.* vi. 8.

† And he grinn'd at the sight, for his favourite vice—1799.

‡ Upon the tree—*Ib.*

§ This anecdote is related by that most interesting of the Devil's biographers, Mr. John Milton, in his *Paradise Lost*, and we have here the Devil's own testimony to the truth and accuracy of it.

"And all amid them stood the tree of life
  High eminent, blooming ambrosial fruit
  Of vegetable gold [query paper money:] and next to Life
  Our Death, the tree of knowledge, grew fast by.—

   \*     \*     \*     \*     \*

So clomb this first grand thief——
Thence up he flew, and on the tree of life
Sat like a cormorant."—*Par. Lost.* iv.

The allegory here is so apt, that in a catalogue of various readings obtained from collating the MSS. one might expect to find it noted, that for "life" *Cod. quid. habent* "trade."

### VIII.

Down the river did glide, with wind and with tide,
  A pig with vast celerity ;
And the Devil look'd wise as he saw how the while,
It cut its own throat.  " There," quoth he with a
    smile,
  " Goes England's commercial prosperity."*

### IX.

As he went through Cold-Bath Fields he saw
  A solitary cell ;
And the Devil was pleased, for it gave him a hint
  For improving his prisons in Hell.

Though indeed the trade, i.e. the bibliopolic, so called κατ'
ἐξόχην, may be regarded as Life *sensu eminentiori ;* a suggestion which I owe to a young retailer in the hosiery line,
who on hearing a description of the net profits, dinner-parties,
country-houses, &c. of the trade, exclaimed, "Ay! that's what
I call Life now !"—This " Life, our Death," is thus happily
contrasted with the fruits of authorship—*Sic nos non nobis
mellificamus apes.*

Of this poem, which with the "Fire, Famine, and Slaughter,"
first appeared in the *Morning Post*, the 1st, 2nd, 3rd, 9th, and
16th stanzas were dictated by Mr. Southey.  See Apologetic
Preface.

    * He saw a pig right rapidly
        Adown the river float,
      The pig swam well, but every stroke
        Was cutting his own throat.

      Old Nicholas grinn'd, and swish'd his tail
        For joy and admiration—
      And he thought of his daughter Victory
        And her darling babe Taxation.—1799.

### X.

He saw a Turnkey in a trice
  Fetter* a troublesome blade;
"Nimbly," quoth he, "do the fingers move
  If a man be but used to his trade."

### XI.

He saw the same Turnkey unfetter a man
  With but little expedition,
Which put him in mind of the long debate†
  On the Slave-trade abolition.

### XII.

He saw an old acquaintance
  As he pass'd by a Methodist meeting;—
She holds a consecrated key,‡
  And the Devil nods her a greeting.

### XIII.

She turn'd up her nose, and said, §
  "Avaunt! my name's Religion,"
And she look'd to Mr.——— ||
  And leer'd like a love-sick pigeon.

* Handcuff—1799.

† And he laugh'd, for he thought of the long debates—*ib.*

‡ He met an old acquaintance
    Just by the Methodist meeting;
  She held a consecrated flag, &c.—*ib.*

§ She tipp'd him the wink, then frown'd and cried,—*ib.*

|| And turn'd to Mr. W———,—*ib.* [Wilberforce presumably.]

XIV.

He saw a certain minister
  (A minister to his mind)
Go up into a certain House,
  With a majority behind.

XV.

The Devil quoted Genesis,
  Like a very learned clerk,
How " Noah and his creeping things
  Went up into the Ark."

XVI.

He took from the poor,
  And he gave to the rich,
And he shook hands with a Scotchman,
  For he was not afraid of the——

XVII.

General————'s burning face
  He saw with consternation,
And back to hell his way did he take,
For the Devil thought by a slight mistake
  It was General Conflagration.*

---

\* If any one should ask who General—— meant, the Author
begs leave to inform him, that he did once see a red-faced
person in a dream whom by the dress he took for a General ;
but he might have been mistaken, and most certainly he did
not hear any names mentioned. In simple verity, the Author
never meant any one, or indeed any thing but to put a concluding stanza to his doggerel.

## THE TWO ROUND SPACES ON
## THE TOMBSTONE.*

THE Devil believes that the Lord will come,
  Stealing a march without beat of drum,
About the same time that he came last
On an old Christmas-day in a snowy blast :
Till he bids the trump sound neither body nor
  soul stirs
For the dead men's heads have slipt under their
  bolsters.


Ho ! ho ! brother Bard, in our churchyard †
Both beds and bolsters are soft and green ;


* This *jeu d' esprit* originally appeared in *The Morning
Post*, December 4, 1800, under the title of " The Two Round
Spaces, a Skeltoniad." Two different versions of it were re-
suscitated in Fraser's Magazine, February and May, 1833, a
circumstance to which we probably owe its inclusion in the
edition of 1834, prefaced by the following note:—

  "This is the first time the author ever published these lines.
He would have been glad had they perished ; but they have
now been printed repeatedly in magazines, and he is told that
the verses will not perish. Here, therefore, they are owned,
with the hope that they will be taken, as assuredly they were
composed, in mere sport."

  † The "brother bard" addressed was presumably Wordsworth, and the " churchyard " that of Grasmere. It was the
sight of Mr. (afterwards Sir James) Mackintosh in that church-
yard that is said to have suggested the lines.—ED.

Save one alone, and that's of stone,
And under it lies a Counsellor keen.
'Twould be a square tomb, if it were not too long,
And 'tis fenced round with irons sharp, spearlike
        and strong.*

This fellow from Aberdeen hither did skip
With a waxy face and a blubber lip,
And a black tooth in front to show in part
What was the colour of his whole heart.
        This Counsellor sweet,
        This Scotchman complete,
    (The Devil scotch him for a snake!)
    I trust he lies in his grave awake.

        On the sixth of January,
    When all around is white with snow
    As a Cheshire yeoman's dairy;
        Brother Bard, ho! ho! believe it, or no,
    On that stone tomb to you I'll show
    [After sunset, and before cock-crow,]
    Two round spaces void of snow. †
I swear by our Knight and his forefathers' souls,
That in size and shape they are just like the holes
        In the house of privity‡
        Of that ancient family.

---

* This tomb would be square, if it were not too long;
    And 'tis rail'd round with iron, tall, spear-like, and strong
                                                1800.

† Clear of snow.—*Ib.*

‡ In the large house of privity—*Ib.*

On those two places void of snow*
There have sat in the night for an hour or so,
Before sunrise, and after cock crow,
(He kicking his heels, she cursing her corns,
All to the tune of the wind in their horns),
    The Devil and his Grannam,
      With a snow-blast to fan 'em ;†
Expecting and hoping the trumpet to blow ;
For they are cock-sure of the fellow below !

## RECANTATION.

ILLUSTRATED IN THE STORY OF THE MAD OX.‡

### I.

A N Ox, long fed with musty hay,
    And work'd with yoke and chain,
Was turn'd out § on an April day,
When fields are in their best array,
And growing grasses sparkle gay
    At once with Sun and rain.

### II.

The grass was fine, the Sun was bright :
    With truth I may aver it ;

---

\* On these two spaces clear of snow—1800.

† With the snow-drift to fan 'em—*Ib.*

‡ Printed in the *The Morning Post*, July 30, 1798.
Reprinted in the second volume of *The Annual Anthology* and
in *Sibylline Leaves.*

§ Was loosen'd—1798.

The Ox was glad, as well he might,
Thought a green meadow no bad sight,
And frisk'd, to shew his huge delight,
     Much like a beast of spirit.


### III.

" *Stop, Neighbours ! stop ! why these alarms ?*
     *The Ox is only glad—* "
But still they pour from cots and farms—
Halloo ! the parish is up in arms,
(A hoaxing-hunt has always charms)
     Halloo ! the Ox is mad.


### IV.

The frighted beast scamper'd about ;
     Plunge ! through the hedge he drove—
The mob pursue with hideous rout,
A bull-dog fastens on his snout ;
He gores the dog, his tongue hangs out ;
     He's mad ! he's mad, by Jove !


### V.

" *Stop, Neighbours, stop !*" aloud did call
     A sage of sober hue.
But all, at once, on him they fall,*
And women squeak and children squall,
" What ! would you have him toss us all ?
     " And damme ! who are you ?"


* " You cruel dog !" at once they bawl—1798.

### VI.

Oh ! hapless sage, his ears they stun,
   And curse him o'er and o'er—
" You bloody-minded dog ! " cries one,
" To slit your windpipe were good fun,—
'Od blast you for an \**impious* son
   Of a presbyterian whore ! "

### VII.

" You'd have him gore the parish-priest,
   And run † against the altar—
You fiend ! " ‡   The sage his warnings ceased,
And north and south, and west and east,
Halloo ! they follow the poor beast,
   Mat, Dick, Tom, Bob and Walter.

### VIII.

Old Lewis ('twas his evil day),
   Stood trembling in his shoes ;
The Ox was his—what could he say ?
His legs were stiffen'd with dismay,
The Ox ran o'er him mid the fray,
   And gave him his death's bruise.

---

  \* One of the many fine words which the most uneducated
had about this time a constant opportunity of acquiring from
the sermons in the pulpit and the proclamations in the ——
corners.

  † Drive—1798.          ‡ Rogue—*Ib*.

IX.

The frighted beast ran on—but here,
  (No tale, tho' in print, more true is) *
My Muse stops short in mid career—
Nay, gentle reader! do not sneer!
I cannot choose but drop a tear,
  A tear for good old Lewis!

X.

The frighted beast ran through the town; †
  All follow'd, boy and dad,
Bull-dog, Parson, Shopman, Clown:
The Publicans rush'd from the Crown,
"Halloo! hamstring him! cut him down!"
  THEY DROVE THE POOR OX MAD.

XI.

Should you a Rat to madness tease
  Why even a Rat may plague you:
There's no Philosopher but sees
That Rage and Fear are one disease—
Though that may burn and this may freeze,
  They're both alike the Ague.

XII.

And so this Ox, in frantic mood,
  Faced round like any Bull—

* The baited ox drove on—but here—
  The gospel scarce more true is—1798.

† The ox drove on right through the town—*Ib.*

The mob turn'd tail, and he pursued,
Till they with heat and fright * were stew'd,
And not a chick of all this brood
  But had his belly full.

### XIII.

Old Nick's astride the beast, 'tis clear—
  Old Nicholas, to a tittle !
But all agree, he'd disappear,
Would but the Parson venture near,
And through his teeth,† right o'er the steer,
  Squirt out some fasting-spittle.

### XIV.

Achilles was a warrior fleet,
  The Trojans he could worry—
Our Parson too was swift of feet,
But shew'd it chiefly in retreat :
The victor Ox scour'd down the street,
  The mob fled hurry-scurry.

### XV.

Through gardens, lanes and fields new-plough'd,
  Through his hedge, and through her hedge,
He plunged and toss'd and bellow'd loud,
Till in his madness he grew proud
To see this helter-skelter crowd
  That had more wrath than courage.

* With fright and fear—1798.

† According to the superstition of the West-Countries, if
you meet the Devil, you may either cut him in half with a
straw, or force him to disappear by spitting over his horns.

### XVI.

Alas! to mend the breaches wide
　He made for these poor ninnies,
They all must work, whate'er betide,
Both days and months, and pay beside
(Sad news for Avarice and for Pride),
　A sight of golden guineas!

### XVII.

But here once more to view did pop
　The man that kept his senses;
And now he cried,—" Stop, neighbours! stop;
The Ox is mad!　I would not swop,
No! not a school-boy's farthing-top
　For all the parish-fences."

### XVIII.

" The Ox is mad!　Ho! Dick, Bob, Mat!"
　" What means this coward fuss?
Ho! stretch this rope across the plat—
'Twill trip him up—or if not that,
Why, damme! we must lay him flat—
　See, here's my blunderbuss.

### XIX.

" *A lying dog!* * *just now he said*
　*The Ox was only glad—*
*Let's break his presbyterian head!*"
" Hush!" quoth the sage, " you've been misled;
No quarrels now—let's all make head—
　YOU DROVE THE POOR OX MAD."

---

\* A barefaced dog!—1798.

### XX.

As thus I sat in careless chat *
  With the morning's wet newspaper,
In eager haste, without his hat,
As blind and blundering as a bat,
In came that fierce aristocrat,
  Our pursy Woollen-draper.

### XXI.

And so my Muse perforce drew bit ;
  And in he rush'd and panted
" Well, have you heard ?"  No, not a whit.
" What, *ha'nt* you heard ?"  Come, out with it !—
" That Tierney votes for Mister Pitt,
  And Sheridan's *recanted !*" †


## TALLEYRAND TO LORD GRENVILLE.

### A METRICAL EPISTLE.‡

[AN unmetrical letter from Talleyrand to Lord
Grenville has already appeared, and from an authority
too high to be questioned : otherwise I could adduce
some arguments for the exclusive authenticity of the
following metrical Epistle.  The very epithet which
the wise ancients used, *aurea carmina,* might have
been supposed likely to have determined the choice of

---

\* But lo ! to interrupt my chat—1798.

† " That Tierney's wounded Mr. Pitt,
  And his fine tongue enchanted ?"—1798.

‡ *Morning Post,* January 10, 1800 ; Coleridge's " Essays
on his own Times," vol. i. pp. 231-237.

the French minister in favour of verse; and the rather when we recollect that this phrase of "golden verses" is applied emphatically to the works of that philosopher who imposed *silence* on all with whom he had to deal. Besides is it not somewhat improbable that Talleyrand should have preferred prose to rhyme, when the latter alone *has got the chink*? Is it not likewise curious that in our official answer no notice whatever is taken of the Chief Consul, Bonaparte, as if there had been no such person existing; notwithstanding that his existence is pretty generally admitted, nay that some have been so rash as to believe that he has created as great a sensation in the world as Lord Grenville, or even the Duke of Portland? But the Minister of Foreign Affairs, Talleyrand, *is* acknowledged, which, in our opinion, could not have happened had he written only that insignificant prose-letter, which seems to precede Bonaparte's, as in old romances a dwarf always ran before to proclaim the advent or arrival of knight or giant. That Talleyrand's character and practices more resemble those of some *regular* Governments than Bonaparte's I admit; but this of itself does not appear a satisfactory explanation. However, let the letter speak for itself. The second line is supererogative in syllables, whether from the oscitancy of the transcriber, or from the trepidation which might have overpowered the modest Frenchman, on finding himself in the act of writing to so *great* a man, I shall not dare to determine. A few Notes are added by

Your servant,

GNOME.

To the Editor of *The Morning Post*.

P.S.—As mottoes are now fashionable, especially if taken from out-of-the-way books, you may prefix, if you please, the following lines from Sidonius Apollinaris :

> *Saxa, et robora, corneasque fibras*
> *Mollit dulciloquâ canorus arte !*]

TALLEYRAND, MINISTER OF FOREIGN AFFAIRS AT
PARIS, TO LORD GRENVILLE, SECRETARY OF
STATE IN GREAT BRITAIN FOR FOREIGN AF-
FAIRS, AUDITOR OF THE EXCHEQUER, A LORD
OF TRADE, AN ELDER BROTHER OF TRINITY
HOUSE, &c.

MY Lord ! though your Lordship repel deviation
From forms long establish'd, yet with high
consideration
I plead for the honour to hope that no blame
Will attach, should this letter *begin* with my name.
I dared not presume on your Lordship to bounce,
But thought it more *exquisite* first to *announce !*
My Lord ! I've the honour to be Talleyrand,
And the letter's from *me !* you'll not draw back
your hand
Nor yet take it up by the rim in dismay,
As boys pick up ha'pence on April fool-day.
I'm no Jacobin foul, or red-hot Cordelier
That your Lordship's *un*gauntleted fingers need
fear
An infection or burn ! Believe me, 'tis true,
With a scorn like your own I look down on the crew
That bawl and hold up to the mob's detestation
The most delicate wish for a *silent persuasion.*
*A form long-establish'd* these Terrorists call

Bribes, perjury, theft, and the devil and all !
And yet spite of all that the * Moralist prates,
'Tis the keystone and cement of *civilized States.*
Those American † *Reps !* And i' faith, they were
　　　serious !
It shock'd us at Paris, like something mysterious,
That men who've a Congress—But no more of 't !
　　　I'm proud
To have stood so distinct from the Jacobin crowd.


　　My Lord ! though the vulgar in wonder be lost at
My transfigurations, and name me *Apostate,*
Such a meaningless nickname, which never in-
　　　censed me,
*Cannot* prejudice you or your Cousin against me :
I'm Ex-bishop.　What then ? Burke himself would
　　　agree
That I left not the Church—'twas the Church that
　　　left me.
My titles prelatic I loved and retain'd,
As long as what *I* meant by Prelate remain'd :
And tho' Mitres no longer will *pass* in our mart,
I'm *episcopal* still to the core of my heart.

---

　* This sarcasm on the writings of moralists is, in general,
extremely just ; but had Talleyrand continued long enough in
England, he might have found an honourable exception in the
second volume of Dr. Paley's Moral Philosophy ; in which
both Secret Influence, and all the other *Established Forms,* are
justified and placed in their true light.

　† A fashionable abbreviation in the higher circles for Re-
publicans.　Thus *Mob* was originally the Mobility.

No  time from my name this my motto shall sever :
'Twill be *Non sine pulvere palma** for ever !

   Your goodness, my Lord, I conceive as excessive,
Or I dared not present  you a scroll so digressive ;
And in truth with my pen  thro' and thro' I should
        strike it ;
But I hear that your Lordship's own style is  just
        like it.
Dear my Lord, we are right : for  what  charms  can
        be show'd
In a thing that goes straight like an old Roman road?
The tortoise crawls straight, the hare doubles about;
And the true line of beauty still winds in and out.
It argues, my Lord ! of fine thoughts such a  brood
        in us
To split and divide into heads multitudinous,
While charms that surprise (it can ne'er be denied
        us)
Sprout forth from each  head, like the  ears  from
        King Midas.
Were a genius of rank, like a commonplace dunce,
Compell'd to drive on to the main point at once,
What a plentiful vintage of initiations †

---

  \* *Palma non sine pulvere.*  In plain English, an itching
palm, not without the yellow dust.

  † The word *Initiations* is borrowed from the new Constitution, and can only mean, in plain English, introductory matter.
If the manuscript would bear us out, we should propose to
read the line thus—" What a plentiful *Verbage*, what Initiations !" inasmuch as Vintage must necessarily refer to wine,

Would Noble Lords lose in your Lordship's orations.
My fancy transports me ! As mute as a mouse,
And as fleet as a pigeon, I'm borne to the House
Where all those who *are* Lords, from father to son,
Discuss the affairs of all those who are none.
I behold you, my Lord ! of your feelings quite full,
'Fore the woolsack arise, like a sack full of wool !
You rise on each Anti-Grenvillian member,
Short, thick and blustrous, like a day in November,*
Short in person, I mean : for the length of your
    speeches
Fame herself, that most famous reporter, ne'er
    reaches.
Lo ! Patience beholds you contemn her brief reign,
And Time, that all-panting toil'd after in vain,
(Like the Beldam who raced for a smock with her
    grandchild)
Drops and cries: ' Were such lungs e'er assign'd to
    a man-child ? '

really or figuratively ; and we cannot guess what species Lord
Grenville's eloquence may be supposed to resemble, unless,
indeed, it be *Cowslip* wine. A slashing critic to whom we
read the manuscript, proposed to read, " What a plenty of
flowers—what initiations ! " and supposes it may allude indis-
criminately to poppy flowers, or flour of brimstone. The
most modest emendation, perhaps, would be this—for Vintage
read Ventage.

   * We cannot sufficiently admire the accuracy of this simile.
For as Lord Grenville, though short, is certainly not the
shortest man in the House, even so is it with the days in
November.

Your strokes at her vitals pale Truth has confess'd,
And Zeal unresisted entempests your breast ! *
Though some noble Lords may be wishing to sup,
Your merit self conscious, my Lord, *keeps you up*,
Unextinguish'd and swoln, as a balloon of paper
Keeps aloft by the smoke of its own farthing taper.
Ye SIXTEENS † of Scotland, your snuffs ye must
    trim ;
Your Geminies, fix'd stars of England ! grow dim,

---

* An evident plagiarism of the ex-Bishop's from Dr. John-
son :—

    "Existence saw him spurn her bounded reign,
    And panting Time toil'd after him in vain :
    His powerful strokes presiding Truth confess'd,
    And unresisting Passion storm'd the breast."

† This line and the following are involved in an almost
Lycophrontic tenebricosity. On repeating them, however, to
an *Illuminant*, whose confidence I possess, he informed me
(and he ought to know, for he is a Tallow-chandler by trade)
that certain candles go by the name of *sixteens*. This explains
the whole, the Scotch Peers are destined to burn out—and so
are candles ! The English are perpetual, and are therefore
styled Fixed Stars ! The word *Geminies* is, we confess, still
obscure to us ; though we venture to suggest that it may
perhaps be a metaphor (daringly sublime) for the two eyes
which noble Lords do in general possess. It is certainly used
by the poet Fletcher in this sense, in the 31st stanza of his
*Purple Island* :—

    "What ! shall I then need seek a patron out,
      Or beg a favour from a mistress' eyes,
    To fence my song against the vulgar rout,
      And shine upon me with her *geminies ?* "

And but for *a form long establish'd*, no doubt
Twinkling faster and faster, ye all would *go out*.

*Apropos*, my dear Lord ! a ridiculous blunder
Of some of our Journalists caused us some wonder :
It was said that in aspect malignant and sinister
In the Isle of Great Britain a great Foreign Minister
Turn'd as pale as a journeyman miller's frock
      coat is
On observing a star that appear'd in Bootes !
When the whole truth was this (O those ignorant
      brutes !)
Your Lordship had made his appearance in boots.
You, my Lord, with your star, sat in boots, and
      the Spanish
Ambassador thereupon thought fit to vanish.
But perhaps, dear my Lord, among other worse
      crimes,
The whole was no more than a lie of *The Times*.
It is monstrous, my Lord ! in a civilized state
That such Newspaper rogues should have license
      to prate.
Indeed printing in general—but for the taxes,
Is in theory false and pernicious in praxis !
You and I, and your Cousin, and Abbé Sieyes,
And all the great Statesmen that live in these days,
Are agreed that no nation secure is from violence
Unless all who must think are maintain'd all in
      silence.
This printing, my Lord—but 'tis useless to mention
What we both of us think—'twas a cursed invention,

And Germany might have been honestly prouder
Had she left it alone, and found out only powder.
My Lord ! when I think of our labours and cares
Who rule the Department of Foreign Affairs,
And how with their libels these journalists bore us,
Though rage I acknowledge than scorn less de-
      corous ;
Yet their presses and types I could shiver in splinters,
Those Printers' black devils ! those devils of
      Printers !
In case of a peace—but perhaps it were better
To proceed to the absolute point of my letter :
For the deep wounds of France, Bonaparte, my
      master,
Has found out a new sort of *basilicon* plaister.
But your time, my dear Lord ! is your nation's best
      treasure,
I've intruded already too long on your leisure ;
If so, I entreat you with penitent sorrow
To pause, and resume the remainder to-morrow.

# A STRANGER MINSTREL.*

[WRITTEN TO MRS. ROBINSON, A FEW WEEKS
BEFORE HER DEATH.]

A S late on Skiddaw's † mount I lay supine,
   Midway th' ascent, in that repose divine
When the soul centred in the heart's recess
Hath quaff'd its fill of Nature's loveliness,
Yet still beside the fountain's marge will stay
   And fain would thirst again, again to quaff;
Then when the tear, slow travelling on its way,
   Fills up the wrinkles ‡ of a silent laugh—
In that sweet mood of sad and humorous thought
A form within me rose, within me wrought
With such strong magic, that I cried aloud,
" Thou ancient Skiddaw by thy helm of cloud,
And by thy many-colour'd chasms deep,§
And by their shadows that for ever sleep,
By yon small flaky mists that love to creep
Along the edges of those spots of light,
Those sunny‖ islands on thy smooth green height,
   And by yon shepherds with their sheep,

---

  * *Memoirs of the late Mrs. Robinson, written by herself.*
*With some posthumous pieces.* Lond. 1801, vol. iv. pp.
141-144; *Poetical Works of the late Mrs. Mary Robinson*,
Lond. 1806; vol. i., xlviii-li. [Now first included in any
collection of Coleridge's Poems.]

  † Skiddaw—1801.       ‡ wrinkle—*ib.*

  § chasms so deep—*ib.*     ‖ sunshine—*ib.*

And dogs and boys, a gladsome crowd,
That rush even now with clamour loud
Sudden from forth thy topmost cloud,
And by this laugh, and by this tear,
I would, old Skiddaw, she were here !
A lady of sweet song is she,
Her soft blue eye was made for thee !
O ancient Skiddaw, by this tear,
I would, I would that she were here !"

Then ancient Skiddaw, stern and proud,
In sullen majesty replying,
Thus spake from out his helm of cloud
(His voice was like an echo dying !) :—
" She dwells belike in* scenes more fair,
And scorns a mount so bleak and bare."

I only sigh'd when this I heard,
Such mournful thoughts within me stirr'd
That all my heart was faint and weak,
So sorely was I troubled !
No laughter wrinkled on† my cheek,
But O the tears were doubled !

But ancient Skiddaw green and high
Heard and understood my sigh ;
And now, in tones less stern and rude,
As if he wish'd to end the feud,
Spake he, the proud response renewing
(His voice was like a monarch wooing) :—

* by—1801.          † now—*ib*.

" Nay, but thou dost not know her might,
　　The pinions of her soul how strong !
But many a stranger in my height
　　Hath sung to me her magic song,
　　　　Sending forth his ecstasy
　　　　In her divinest melody,
　　And hence I know her soul is free,
　　She is where'er she wills to be,
　　　Unfetter'd by mortality !
Now to the ' haunted beach' can fly,
　　Beside the threshold scourged with waves,
　　Now where the maniac wildly raves,*
" *Pale moon, thou spectre of the sky !* "
　　No wind that hurries o'er my height
　　Can travel with so swift a flight.
　　　　I too, methinks, might merit
　　　　The presence of her spirit !
　　　　To me too might belong
　　The honour of her song and witching melody,
　　　　Which most resembles me,
　　　　Soft, various, and sublime,
　　　　Exempt from wrongs of Time !"

　　Thus spake the mighty Mount, and I
　　Made answer, with a deep-drawn sigh :—
　　" Thou ancient Skiddaw, by this tear,
　　I would, I would that she were here !"
*November*, 1800.

* Now to the maniac while he raves—1801.

# EPIGRAMS.

# TO MR. PYE*

On his *Carmen Seculare* (a title which has by various persons who have heard it, been thus translated, " A Poem *an age long* ").

> Your Poem must *eternal* be,
>    *Eternal!* it can't fail,
> For 'tis *incomprehensible*,
>    And without head or tail ! †

---

\* *Morning Post*, Jan. 24, 1800.

† " The following anecdote will not be wholly out of place here, and may perhaps amuse the reader. An amateur performer in verse expressed to a common friend, a strong desire to be introduced to me, but hesitated in accepting my friend's immediate offer, on the score that " he was, he must acknowledge, the author of a confounded severe epigram on my *Ancient Mariner*, which had given me great pain. I assured my friend that if the epigram was a good one, it would only increase my desire to become acquainted with the author, and begged to hear it recited : when, to my no less surprise than amusement, it proved to be one which I had myself some time before written and inserted in the *Morning Post*.

> To the author of the *Ancient Mariner*.
>        Your poem must eternal be,
>        Dear sir ! it cannot fail,
>        For 'tis incomprehensible
>        And without head or tail."

—*Biographia Literaria*, Lond. 1817, vol. i. p. 28. It would seem, however, from the above that it was an afterthought on the author's part to apply this epigram to himself and his *Ancient Mariner*.—ED.

## EPIGRAMS.*

### I.

O WOULD the Baptist come again
    And preach aloud with might and main
Repentance to our viperous race!
But should this miracle take place,
I hope, ere Irish ground he treads,
He'll lay in a good stock of heads!

### II.

#### OCCASIONED BY THE FORMER.

I HOLD of all our viperous race
    The greedy creeping things in place
Most vile, most venomous; and then
The United Irishmen!
To come on earth should John determine,
Imprimis, we'll excuse his sermon.
Without a word the good old Dervis
Might work incalculable service,
At once from tyranny and riot
Save laws, lives, liberties and moneys,
If sticking to his ancient diet
He'd but eat up our locusts and *wild honeys!*

### III.

#### ON A READER OF HIS OWN VERSES.†

H OARSE MÆVIUS reads his hobbling verse
    To all and at all times,

* *Annual Anthology*, Vol. II. Bristol, 1800.
† *Morning Post*, Sept. 7, 1799; *Keepsake*, 1829.

And deems them both divinely smooth,
　　His voice as well as rhymes.

But folks say, Mævius is no ass !
　　But Mævius makes it clear
That he's a monster of an ass,
　　An ass without an ear.

### IV.

IF the guilt of all lying consists in deceit
　　Lie on—'tis your duty, sweet youth !
For believe me, then only we find you a cheat
　　When you cunningly tell us the truth.

### V.*

JACK drinks fine wines, wears modish clothing,
　　But prithee where lies Jack's estate?
In Algebra, for there I found of late
A quantity call'd less than nothing.

### VI.

AS Dick and I at Charing Cross were walking
　　Whom should we see on t'other side pass by
But Informator with a stranger talking,
　　So I exclaim'd, " Lord what a lie !"
Quoth Dick—" What, can you hear him ?"
　　" Hear him ! stuff !
I saw him open his mouth—an't that enough ?"

---

\* *Morning Post*, Nov. 16, 1799.

## VII.

### TO A PROUD PARENT.

THY babes ne'er greet thee with the father's
    name ;
  ' My Lud !' they lisp.   Now whence can this
    arise ?
Perhaps their mother feels an honest shame
    And will not teach her infant to tell lies.

## VIII.

HIPPONA lets no silly flush
    Disturb her cheek, nought makes her blush.
Whate'er obscenities you say
She nods and titters frank and gay.
Oh Shame awake one honest flush
For this,—that nothing makes her blush.

## IX.

THY lap-dog, Rufa, is a dainty beast,
    It don't surprise me in the least
To see thee lick so dainty clean a beast.
But that so dainty clean a beast licks thee,
Yes—that surprises me.

## X.*

JEM writes his verses with more speed
    Than the printer's boy can set 'em ;
Quite as fast as we can read,
    And only not so fast as we forget 'em.

* *Morning Post*, Sept. 23, 1799.

### XI.*

DORIS can find no taste in tea,
  Green to her drinks like Bohea;
Because she makes the tea so small
She never tastes the tea at all.

### XII.

WHAT? rise again with *all* one's bones?
  Quoth Giles, I hope you fib?
I trusted when I went to Heaven
  To go without my rib.

### XIII.

#### ON A BAD SINGER.

SWANS sing before they die—'twere no bad
  thing
Should certain persons die before they sing.

### XIV.

#### OCCASIONED BY THE LAST.

A JOKE (cries Jack) without a sting—
  *Post obitum* can no man sing.
And true, if Jack don't mend his manners
And quit the atheistic banners,
*Post obitum* will Jack run foul
Of such *folks* as can only *howl*.

### XV.

#### ON A MODERN DRAMATIST.

NOT for the Stage his plays are fit,
  But suit the closet, said a wit.

* *Morning Post*, Nov. 14, 1799.

The closet? said his friend, I ween
The water-closet 'tis you mean.

### XVI.

TO be ruled like a Frenchman the Briton is loth
 Yet in truth a *direct-tory* governs them both.
1798.

### XVII.

#### ON A VERY UGLY WOMAN.

HOW happy for us mortals 'twere
    Had Eve been such a woman !
The Devil ne'er had tempted her
    And she had tempted no man.

———

There comes from old Avaro's grave
    A deadly stench—why, sure they have
Immured his *soul* within his grave?

———

Last Monday all the papers said
    That Mr. —— was dead ;
    Why, then, what said the city?
The tenth part sadly shook their head,
And shaking sigh'd and sighing said,
    " Pity, indeed, 'tis pity !"

But when the said report was found
A rumour wholly without ground,
    Why, then, what said the city?
The other *nine* parts shook their head,
Repeating what the tenth had said,
    " Pity, indeed, 'tis pity !"*

* *The Keepsake*, 1829.

## TO A CRITIC*

### WHO QUOTED AN ISOLATED PASSAGE, AND THEN DECLARED IT UNINTELLIGIBLE.

MOST candid critic, what if I,
    By way of joke, pluck out your eye,
And holding up the fragment cry,
    " Ha ! ha ! that men such fools should be !
Behold this shapeless mass !—and he
Who own'd it, dreamt that it could see !"
The joke were mighty analytic,
But should you like it, candid critic ?

## SONG

### TO BE SUNG BY THE LOVERS OF ALL THE NOBLE LIQUORS COMPRISED UNDER THE NAME OF ALE. †

#### A.

YE drinkers of Stingo and Nappy so free,
    Are the Gods on Olympus so happy [as] we ?

#### B.

    They cannot be so happy !
    For why ? they drink no Nappy.

---

* Originally printed in the *Morning Post*, Dec. 16, 1801, with the heading, " To a Critic who extracted a passage from a poem without adding a word respecting the context, and then derided it as unintelligible." Reprinted in *The Keepsake*, 1829, as above, with the author's name.

† *Morning Post*, Sept. 18, 1801.

A.

But what if Nectar, in their lingo,
Is but another name for Stingo?

B.

Why, then we and the Gods are equally blest,
And Olympus an Ale-house as good as the best!

## EPITAPH
### ON A BAD MAN.*

OF him that in this gorgeous tomb doth lie
    This sad brief tale is all that Truth can give—
He lived like one who never thought to die,
    He died like one who dared not hope to live!

## DRINKING VERSUS THINKING;
### OR, A SONG AGAINST THE NEW PHILOSOPHY.†

MY Merry men all, that drink with glee
    This fanciful Philosophy,
        Pray tell me what good is it?
If *antient Nick* should come and take
The same across the Stygian Lake,
        I guess we ne'er should miss it.

Away, each pale, self-brooding spark
That goes truth-hunting in the dark,
        Away from our carousing!

* *Morning Post*, Sept. 22, 1801.
† *Ibid*, Sept. 25, 1801.

To Pallas we resign such fowls—
Grave birds of wisdom ! yc're but owls,
    And all your trade but *mousing !*

My Merry men all, here's punch and wine,
And spicy bishop, drink divine !
    Let's live while we are able.
While Mirth and Sense sit, hand in glove,
This Don Philosophy we'll shove
    Dead drunk beneath the table !

## A HINT TO PREMIERS AND FIRST CONSULS.\*

### FROM AN OLD TRAGEDY, VIZ. AGATHA TO KING ARCHELAUS.

THREE truths should make thee often think
    and pause ;
The first is, that thou govern'st over men ;
The second, that thy power is from the laws ;
    And this the third, that thou must die !—and
        then ?—

## THE WILLS OF THE WISP.

### A SAPPHIC. †

*Vix ea nostra voco.*

LUNATIC Witch-fires ! Ghosts of Light and
    Motion !
Fearless I see you weave your wanton dances

---

\* *Morning Post*, Sept. 27, 1802 ; Coleridge's " Essays on
his own Times," III. 992.

† *Morning Post*, December 1, 1801.

Near me, far off me ; you, that tempt the traveller
              Onward and onward.

Wooing, retreating, till the swamp beneath him
Groans—and 'tis dark !—This woman's wile—
    I know it !
Learnt it from *thee*, from *thy* perfidious glances !
              Black-eyed Rebecca !


## WESTPHALIAN SONG.*

[The following is an almost literal translation of a
very old and very favourite song among the Westphalian Boors.   The turn at the end is the same with one
of Mr. Dibdin's excellent songs, and the air to which
it is sung by the Boors is remarkably sweet and lively.]

WHEN thou to my true-love comest
      Greet her from me kindly ;
When she asks thee how I fare ?
      Say, folks in Heaven fare finely.

When she asks, " What ! Is he sick ? "
      Say, dead !—and when for sorrow
She begins to sob and cry,
      Say, I come to-morrow.


* *Morning Post*, Sept. 27, 1802 ; Coleridge's "Essays on
his own Times:" vol. III. p. 992.

## ORIGINAL EPIGRAMS.*

WHAT is an Epigram? a dwarfish whole,
 Its body brevity, and wit its soul.

———

CHARLES, grave or merry, at no lie would stick,
 And taught at length his memory the same
  trick.
Believing thus what he so oft repeats
He's brought the thing to such a pass, poor youth,
 That now himself and no one else he cheats,
Save when unluckily he tells the truth.

———

AN evil spirit's on thee, friend! of late—
 Ev'n from the hour thou camest to thy estate.
Thy mirth all gone, thy kindness, thy discretion,
Th' estate has proved to thee a most complete
  possession.                    [blest,
Shame, shame, old friend! would'st thou be truly
Be thy wealth's lord, not slave! *possessor*, not
  *possess'd*.

———

HERE lies the Devil—ask no other name.
 Well—but you mean Lord—? Hush! we
  mean the same.

———

* Printed in *The Morning Post*, Sept. 23 and Oct. 2, 9, 11,
1802.

## TO ONE WHO PUBLISHED IN PRINT

### WHAT HAD BEEN ENTRUSTED TO HIM
### BY MY FIRESIDE.

TWO things hast thou made known to half the
    nation,
My secrets and my want of penetration :
For O ! far more than all which thou hast penn'd
It shames me to have call'd a wretch like thee my
    friend !

-----

    *" Obscuri sub luce maligna."* VIRG.

SCARCE any scandal, but has a handle ;
    In truth most falsehoods have their rise ;
Truth first unlocks Pandora's box,
    And out there fly a host of lies.
Malignant light, by cloudy night,
    To precipices it decoys one !
One nectar-drop from Jove's own shop
    Will flavour a whole cup of poison.

-----

\* HOW seldom, friend ! a good great man in-
    herits
Honour or wealth with all his worth and pains !
It sounds like stories from the land of spirits
If any man obtain that which he merits
    Or any merit that which he obtains.

  \* This and the reply to it were reprinted in *The Friend*,
Dec. 28, 1809.

### REPLY TO THE ABOVE.

FOR shame, dear friend, renounce this canting
　　strain !
What would'st thou have a good great man obtain ?
Place ? titles ? salary ? a gilded chain ?
Or throne of corses which his sword had slain ?
Greatness and goodness are not *means*, but *ends !*
Hath he not always treasures, always friends,
The good great man ? *three* treasures, LOVE, and
　　LIGHT,
　And CALM THOUGHTS, regular as infant's breath :
And three firm friends, more sure than day and
　　night,
　　HIMSELF, his MAKER, and the ANGEL DEATH !

---

OLD HARPY jeers at castles in the air,
　　And thanks his stars, whenever Edmund
　　　speaks,
That such a dupe as that is not his heir—
　But know, old Harpy ! that these fancy freaks
Though vain and light, as floating gossamer,
Always amuse, and sometimes mend the heart :
　A young man's idlest hopes are still his pleasures,
And fetch a higher price in Wisdom's mart
　Than all the unenjoying Miser's treasures.

### TO A VAIN YOUNG LADY.

DIDST thou think less of thy dear self
　　Far more would others think of thee !

Sweet Anne ! the knowledge of thy wealth
　　Reduces thee to poverty.
Boon Nature gave wit, beauty, health,
　　On thee as on her darling pitching ;
Couldst thou forget thou'rt thus enrich'd
　　That moment would'st thou become rich in !
And wert thou not so self-bewitch'd,
　　Sweet Anne ! thou wert, indeed, bewitching.

———

FROM me, Aurelia ! you desired
　　Your proper praise to know ;
Well ! you're the Fair by all admired—
　　Some twenty years ago.

### FOR A HOUSE-DOG'S COLLAR.

WHEN thieves come, I bark : when gallants, I
　　am still—
So perform both my master's and mistress's will.

———

IN vain I praise thee, Zoilus !
　　In vain thou rail'st at me !
Me no one credits Zoilus !
　　And no one credits thee !

### EPITAPH ON A MERCENARY MISER.

A POOR benighted Pedlar knock'd
　　One night at Sell-all's door,

The same who saved old Sell-all's life—
    'Twas but the year before !
And Sell-all rose and let him in,
    Not utterly unwilling,
But first he bargain'd with the man,
    And took his only shilling !
That night he dreamt he'd given away his pelf,
Walk'd in his sleep, and sleeping hung himself !
And now his soul and body rest below ;
    And here they say his punishment and fate is
To lie awake and every hour to know
    How many people read his tombstone GRATIS.


## A DIALOGUE BETWEEN AN AUTHOR AND HIS FRIEND.

*Author.* Come ; your opinion of my manuscript !
*Friend.* Dear Joe ! I would almost as soon be whipt.
*Author.* But I *will* have it !
*Friend.* If it must be had—*(hesitating)*
You write so ill, I scarce could read the hand—
*Author.* A mere evasion !
*Friend.* And you spell so bad,
That what I read I could not understand.


## Μωροσοφια, OR WISDOM IN FOLLY.

TOM SLOTHFUL talks, as slothful Tom
    beseems,
    What he shall shortly gain and what be doing,

Then drops asleep, and so prolongs his dreams
  And thus *enjoys* at once what half the world are
    *wooing.*

———

EACH Bond-street buck conceits, unhappy elf!
  He shews his clothes! Alas! he shows *himself.*
O that they knew, these overdrest self-lovers,
What hides the body oft the mind discovers.

## FROM AN OLD GERMAN POET.

THAT France has put us oft to rout
  With *powder*, which ourselves found out;
And laughs at us for fools in *print*
Of which our genius was the mint;
All this I easily admit,
For we have genius, France has wit.
But 'tis too bad, that blind and mad
To Frenchmen's wives each travelling German goes,
  Expands his manly vigour by *their* sides,
Becomes the father of his country's foes
  And turns *their warriors* oft to parricides.

## ON THE CURIOUS CIRCUMSTANCE

### THAT IN THE GERMAN LANGUAGE THE SUN IS FEMININE AND THE MOON MASCULINE.

OUR English poets, bad and good, agree
  To make the Sun a male, the Moon a she.

He drives HIS dazzling diligence on high,
In verse, as constantly as in the sky ;
And cheap as blackberries our sonnets show
The Moon, Heaven's huntress, with HER silver bow ;
By which they'd teach us, if I guess aright,
Man rules the day, and woman rules the night.
In Germany they just reverse the thing ;
The Sun becomes a queen, the Moon a king.
Now, that the Sun should represent the women,
The Moon the men, to me seem'd mighty humming ;
And when I first read German, made me stare.
Surely it is not that the wives are there
As *common* as the Sun to lord and loon,
And all their husbands *horned* as the Moon.

## SPOTS IN THE SUN.

MY father confessor is strict and holy,
  *Mi Fili*, still he cries, *peccare noli.*
And yet how oft I find the pious man
At Annette's door, the lovely courtesan !
Her soul's deformity the good man wins
And not her charms ! he comes to hear her sins !
Good father ! I would fain not do thee wrong ;
But ah ! I fear that they who oft and long
Stand gazing at the sun, to count each spot,
*Must* sometimes find the sun itself too hot.

———

WHEN Surface talks of other people's worth
  He has the weakest memory on earth !

And when his own good deeds he deigns to
    mention,
His *memory* still is no whit better grown ;
But then he makes up for it, all will own,
    By a prodigious talent of *invention.*


## TO MY CANDLE.—THE FAREWELL
## EPIGRAM.

GOOD Candle, thou that with thy brother, Fire,
    Art my best friend and comforter at night,
Just snuff'd, thou look'st as if thou didst desire
    That I on thee an epigram should write.
Dear Candle, burnt down to a finger-joint,
    Thy own flame is an epigram of sight ;
    'Tis *short*, and *pointed*, and *all over* light,
Yet gives *most* light and burns the keenest at
        the point.                *Valete et Plaudite.*

———

AN excellent adage commands that we should
    Relate of the dead that alone which is good ;
But of the great Lord who here lies in lead
We know nothing good but that he is dead.*

* *The Friend*, No. 12, Nov. 9, 1809 (where five of the above
Epigrams are reprinted).

SIBYLLINE LEAVES.

# SIBYLLINE LEAVES.

## LINES TO W. L., ESQ.,

### WHILE HE SANG A SONG TO PURCELL'S MUSIC.*

WHILE my young cheek retains its healthful hues,
　　And I have many friends who hold me dear,
　　I,——! methinks, I would not often hear
Such melodies as thine, lest I should lose
All memory of the wrongs and sore distress
　　For which my miserable brethren weep !
　　But should uncomforted misfortunes steep
My daily bread in tears and bitterness ;
And if at death's dread moment I should lie
　　With no beloved face at my bed-side,
To fix the last glance of my closing eye, 　　[guide,
　　Methinks such strains, breathed by my angel-
Would make me pass the cup of anguish by,
　　Mix with the blest, nor know that I had died !

## TO AN UNFORTUNATE WOMAN
## AT THE THEATRE.†

MAIDEN,‡ that with sullen brow
　　Sitt'st behind those virgins gay,

---

\* Printed in the second volume of *The Annual Anthology*,
Bristol, 1800.

† *Annual Anthology*, Bristol, 1800.　　‡ Sufferer—1800.

Like a scorch'd and mildew'd bough,
  Leafless 'mid the blooms of May!

Him who lured thee and forsook,
  Oft I watch'd with angry gaze,
Fearful saw his pleading look,
  Anxious heard his fervid phrase.

Soft the glances of the youth,
  Soft his speech, and soft his sigh;
But no sound like simple truth,
  But no true love in his eye.*

Loathing thy polluted lot,
  Hie thee, Maiden,† hie thee hence!
Seek thy weeping Mother's cot,
  With a wiser innocence.

Thou hast known deceit and folly,
  Thou hast felt, that vice is woe:
With a musing melancholy
  Inly arm'd, go, Maiden! go.

---

* The second and third stanzas have replaced the following
in the original version :—

  " Inly gnawing, thy distresses
      Mock those starts of wanton glee,
    And thy inmost soul confesses
      Chaste affliction's majesty."

† Sufferer—1800.

Mother sage of self-dominion,
  Firm thy steps, O Melancholy !
The strongest plume in Wisdom's pinion
  Is the memory of past folly.

Mute the sky-lark * and forlorn,
  While she moults the firstling plumes,
That had skimm'd the tender corn,
  Or the beanfield's odorous blooms.

Soon with renovated wing
  Shall she dare a loftier flight,
Upward to the day-star spring,
  And embathe in heavenly light.

## LINES COMPOSED IN A CONCERT-ROOM.†

NOR cold, nor stern, my soul ! yet I detest
    These scented rooms, where, to a gaudy
      throng,
Heaves the proud harlot her distended breast
  In intricacies of laborious song.

These feel not Music's genuine power, nor deign
    To melt at Nature's passion-warbled plaint,
But when the long-breathed singer's uptrill'd strain
  Bursts in a squall—they gape for wonderment.

* The lavrock—1800.
† *Morning Post*, September 24, 1799.

Hark ! the deep buzz of vanity and hate !
　　Scornful, yet envious, with self-torturing sneer
My lady eyes some maid of humbler state,
　　While the pert captain, or the primmer priest,
　　Prattles accordant scandal in her ear.

O give me, from this heartless scene * released,
　　To hear our old musician, blind and gray,
(Whom stretching from my nurse's arms I kiss'd,)
　　His Scottish tunes and warlike marches play,
　　By moonshine, on the balmy summer-night,
　　The while I dance amid the tedded hay
With merry maids, whose ringlets toss in light.

Or lies the purple evening on the bay
Of the calm glossy lake ?　O let me hide
　　Unheard, unseen, behind the alder-trees,
For round their roots † the fisher's boat is tied,
　　On whose trim seat doth Edmund stretch at ease,
And while the lazy boat sways to and fro,
　　Breathes in his flute sad airs, so wild and slow,
That his own cheek is wet with quiet tears.

But O, dear Anne ! when midnight wind careers,
And the gust pelting on the out-house shed
　　Makes the cock shrilly in the rain-storm crow,
　　To hear thee sing some ballad full of woe,
Ballad of shipwreck'd sailor floating dead,
　　Whom his own true-love buried in the sands !

　　* Loathsome scene—1799.
　　† Around whose roots—*ib.*

Thee, gentle woman, for thy voice re-measures
Whatever tones and melancholy pleasures
   The things of Nature utter; birds or trees,
Or moan of ocean-gale in weedy caves,
Or where the stiff grass mid the heath-plant waves,
   Murmur and music thin of sudden breeze.

[Dear Maid! whose form in solitude I seek,
   Such songs in such a mood to hear thee sing,
   It were a deep delight!—But thou shalt fling
Thy white arm round my neck, and kiss my cheek,
   And love the brightness of my gladder eye,
   The while I tell thee what a holier joy

It were, in proud and stately step to go,
   With trump and timbrel clang, and popular shout,
   To celebrate the shame and absolute rout
Unhealable of Freedom's latest foe,
   Whose tower'd might shall to its centre nod.

When human feelings, sudden, deep and vast,
As all good spirits of all ages past
   Were armied in the hearts of living men,
Shall purge the earth and violently sweep
These vile and painted locusts to the deep,
Leaving un——————— undebased,
A ——— world, made worthy of its God.]*

* The two last lines appear exactly thus in the newspaper
from which they are derived. It would be a fruitless waste of
ingenuity to attempt by conjecture to fill up the hiatuses, or to
decide whether they were intentional or arose from the illegibility
of the Author's MS.—ED.

## THE KEEPSAKE.*

THE tedded hay, the first fruits of the soil,
    The tedded hay and corn-sheaves in one field,
Show summer gone, ere come.   The foxglove tall
Sheds its loose purple bells, or in the gust,
Or when it bends beneath the up-springing lark,
Or mountain-finch alighting.   And the rose
(In vain the darling of successful love)
Stands, like some boasted beauty of past years,
The thorns remaining, and the flowers all gone.
Nor can I find, amid my lonely walk
By rivulet, or spring, or wet road-side,
That blue and bright-eyed floweret of the brook,
Hope's gentle gem, the sweet forget-me-not ! †
So will not fade the flowers which Emmeline
With delicate fingers on the snow-white silk
Has work'd (the flowers which most she knew I
    loved,)
And, more beloved than they,‡ her auburn hair.

* Printed in *The Morning Post*, September 17, 1802.

† One of the names (and meriting to be the only one) of
the *Myosotis Scorpioides Palustris*, a flower from six to twelve
inches high, with blue blossom and bright yellow eye.   It
has the same name over the whole Empire of Germany *(Ver-
gissmein nicht)* and, I believe, in Denmark and Sweden.

‡ More beloved than all—1802.

In the cool morning twilight, early waked
By her full bosom's joyous restlessness,
[Leaving the soft bed to her sister]
Softly she rose, and lightly stole along,
[Her fair face flushing in the purple dawn]
Down the slope coppice to the woodbine bower, *
Whose rich flowers, swinging in the morning breeze,
Over their dim fast-moving shadows hung,
Making a quiet image of disquiet
In the smooth, scarcely moving † river-pool.
There, in that bower where first she own'd her love,
And let me kiss my own warm tear of joy
From off her glowing cheek, she sat and stretch'd
The silk upon the frame, and work'd her name
Between the moss-rose and forget-me-not—
Her own dear name, with her own auburn hair !
That forced to wander till sweet spring return,
I yet might ne'er forget her smile, her look,
Her voice, (that even in her mirthful mood
Has made me wish to steal away and weep,)
Nor yet the entrancement of that maiden kiss
With which she promised that when spring
        return'd
She would resign one half of that dear name,
And own thenceforth no other name but mine !

* Adown the meadow to the woodbine bower—1802.

† Scarcely-flowing—*Ib.*

## THE DAY-DREAM.*

FROM AN EMIGRANT TO HIS ABSENT WIFE.

I F thou wert here, these tears were tears of light !
  But from as sweet a vision did I start
As ever made these eyes grow idly bright !
  And though I weep, yet still around my heart
A sweet and playful tenderness doth linger,
Touching my heart as with an infant's finger.

My mouth half open, like a witless man,
  I saw our couch, I saw our quiet room,
  Its shadows heaving by the fire-light gloom ;
And o'er my lips a subtle feeling ran,
All o'er my lips a soft and breeze-like feeling—
I know not what—but had the same been stealing

Upon a sleeping mother's lips, I guess
  It would have made the loving mother dream
That she was softly bending down to kiss
  Her babe, that something more than babe did
    seem,
A floating presence of its darling father,
And yet its own dear baby self far rather !

Across my chest there lay a weight, so warm !
  As if some bird had taken shelter there ;

* Printed in *The Morning Post*, October 19, 1802.

And lo! I seem'd to see a woman's form—
   Thine, Sara, thine? O joy, if thine it were!
I gazed with stifled breath, and fear'd to stir it,
No deeper trance e'er wrapt a yearning spirit!

And now, when I seem'd sure thy face to see,
   Thy own dear self in our own quiet home;
There came an elfish laugh, and waken'd me:
'Twas Frederic, who behind my chair had clomb,
And with his bright eyes at my face was peeping.
I bless'd him, tried to laugh, and fell a-weeping!

## TO A YOUNG LADY.

### ON HER RECOVERY FROM A FEVER.*

WHY need I say, Louisa dear!
   How glad I am to see you here,
  A lovely convalescent;
Risen from the bed of pain and fear,
  And feverish heat incessant.

The sunny showers, the dappled sky,
The little birds that warble high,†

---

\* Printed in *The Morning Post*, December 9, 1799, and in *The Annual Anthology*, vol. ii., Bristol, 1800. The lines are there entitled " To a Young Lady on her first appearance after a dangerous illness," written in the spring, 1799. The young lady is named Ophelia in the original version of the poem.—ED.

† The breezy air, the sun, the sky,
   The little birds that sing on high—1799.

Their vernal loves commencing,
Will better welcome you than I
    With their sweet influencing.

Believe me, while in bed you lay,
Your danger taught us all to pray :
    You made us grow devouter ! *
Each eye look'd up and seem'd to say,
    How can we do without her?

Besides, what vex'd us worse, we knew
They have no need of such as you †
    In the place where you were going :
This world has angels all too few,
    And Heaven is overflowing !


## SOMETHING CHILDISH, BUT VERY NATURAL.

### WRITTEN IN GERMANY. ‡

IF I had but two little wings
    And were a little feathery bird,
        To you I'd fly, my dear !
But thoughts like these are idle things,
        And I stay here.

---

* Your danger taught us how to pray ;
    You made us all devouter—1799.
† Besides (which vex'd us worse) we knew
    They had no need of such as you—*ib.*
‡ *Annual Anthology*, Bristol, 1800.

But in my sleep to you I fly :
  I'm always with you in my sleep !
    The world is all one's own.
But then one wakes, and where am I ?
    All, all alone.

Sleep stays not, though a monarch bids :
  So I love to wake ere break of day :
    For though my sleep be gone,
Yet while 'tis dark, one shuts one's lids,
    And still dreams on.


## HOME-SICK.

### WRITTEN IN GERMANY.*

'Tis sweet to him who all the week
    Through city-crowds must push his way,
To stroll alone through fields and woods,
    And hallow thus the Sabbath-day.

And sweet it is in summer bower,
    Sincere, affectionate and gay,
One's own dear children feasting round,
    To celebrate one's marriage-day.

But what is all to his delight
    Who having long been doom'd to roam,

* *Annual Anthology*, Bristol, 1800.

Throws off the bundle from his back,
 Before the door of his own home?

Home-sickness is a wasting pang;*
 This feel I hourly more and more:
There's healing only in thy wings,
 Thou Breeze that play'st on Albion's shore!


## ANSWER TO A CHILD'S QUESTION. †

DO you ask what the birds say? The sparrow, the
  dove,
The linnet and thrush say, " I love and I love!"
In the winter they're silent—the wind is so strong—
What it says I don't know, but it sings a loud song.
But green leaves, and blossoms, and sunny warm
  weather,
And singing, and loving—all come back together.
[" I love, and I love," almost all the birds say
From sunrise to star-rise, so gladsome are they!]
But the lark is so brimful of gladness and love,
The green fields below him, the blue sky above,
That he sings, and he sings; and for ever sings he—
" I love my Love, and my Love loves me!"
['Tis no wonder that he's full of joy to the brim,
When he loves his Love, and his Love loves him!]

---

 * Is no baby pang;—1800.

 † Printed in *The Morning Post*, October 16, 1802, with the
following title:—"The Language of Birds: Lines spoken
extempore to a little child in early spring."

## ON REVISITING THE SEA-SHORE,

### AFTER LONG ABSENCE, UNDER STRONG MEDICAL RECOMMENDATION NOT TO BATHE.*

GOD be with thee, gladsome Ocean !
  How gladly greet I thee once more !
Ships and waves, and ceaseless motion,
  And men rejoicing on thy shore. †

Dissuading spake the mild physician,
  " Those briny waves for thee are death !" ‡
But my soul fulfill'd her mission,
  And lo ! I breathe untroubled breath !

Fashion's pining sons and daughters,
  That seek the crowd they seem to fly, §
Trembling they approach thy waters ;
  And what cares Nature if they die ?

Me a thousand hopes ‖ and pleasures,
  A thousand recollections bland,

---

* Printed in *The Morning Post*, September 15, 1801, and
there entitled, " Ode after bathing in the sea, contrary to
medical advice."

  † Ships, and waves, and endless motion,
    And life rejoicing on thy shore.—1801.

  ‡ Mildly said the mild physician
    To bathe me on thy shores were death ;—*ib.*

  § That love the City's gilded sty—*ib.*          ‖ Loves—*ib.*

Thoughts sublime, and stately measures,
  Revisit on thy echoing strand : *

Dreams (the soul herself forsaking,)
  Tearful raptures,† boyish mirth ;
Silent adorations, making
  A blessed shadow of this Earth !

O ye hopes that stir within me,
  Health comes with you from above !
God is with me, God is in me !
  I cannot die, if Life be Love.


## HYMN BEFORE SUN-RISE,

### IN THE VALE OF CHAMOUNI.‡

[Chamouni is one of the highest mountain valleys
of the Barony of Faucigny in the Savoy Alps; and
exhibits a kind of fairy world, in which the wildest
appearances (I had almost said horrors) of Nature
alternate with the softest and most beautiful. The
chain of Mont Blanc is its boundary ; and besides the

---

\* Sounding strand—1801.    † Grieflike transports—*ib.*

‡ First printed in *The Morning Post*, Saturday, September 11,
1802, with the title of " Chamouni, the Hour before Sunrise,
a Hymn ;" reprinted with many alterations in *The Friend* of
October 26, 1809.

" The Hymn to Chamouni," says De Quincey (*Tait's Magazine*, Sept. 1834), " is an expansion of a short poem in stanzas
upon the same subject by Frederica Brun, a female poet of
Germany, previously known to the world under her maiden

Arvè it is filled with sounds from the Arveiron, which
rushes from the melted glaciers, like a giant, mad with
joy, from a dungeon, and forms other torrents of
snow-water, having their rise in the glaciers which
slope down into the valley. The beautiful *gentiana
major*, or greater gentian, with blossoms of the
brightest blue, grows in large companies a few steps
from the never-melted ice of the glaciers. I thought
it an affecting emblem of the boldness of human hope,
venturing near, and, as it were, leaning over the brink
of the grave. Indeed, the whole vale, its every light,
its every sound, must needs impress every mind not
utterly callous with the thought—Who *would* be, who
*could* be an Atheist in this valley of wonders! If any
of (my) readers have visited this vale in their journeys
among the Alps, I am confident that they will not find
the sentiments and feelings expressed, or attempted
to be expressed, in the following poem, extravagant.]

HAST thou a charm to stay the morning star
  In his steep course? So long he seems to
    pause
On thy bald awful head,* O sovran Blanc ! †
The Arve and Arveiron at thy base
Rave ceaselessly ; but thou, most awful Form ! ‡

name of Münter. The mere framework of the poem is exactly
the same. . . . On the other hand, by a judicious ampli-
fication of some topics, and by its far deeper tone of lyrical
enthusiasm, the dry bones of the German outline have been
created by Coleridge into the fulness of life. It is not, therefore, a paraphrase, but a recast of the original."

 * Top—1809.     † O Chamouni !—1802.

  ‡ Dread mountain form !—1802. Dread awful form !—1809.

Risest from forth thy silent sea of pines,
How silently !   Around thee and above
Deep is the air and dark, substantial, black,*
An ebon mass : methinks thou piercest it,
As with a wedge !   But when I look again,
It is thine own calm home, thy crystal shrine,
Thy habitation from eternity !
O dread and silent Mount ! † I gazed upon thee,
Till thou, still present to the bodily sense,‡
Didst vanish from my thought : entranced in prayer
I worshipp'd the Invisible alone.

Yet, like some sweet beguiling melody,
So sweet, we know not we are listening to it,
Thou, the meanwhile, wast blending with my
    thought,
Yea, with my life and life's own secret joy :
Till the dilating Soul, enrapt, transfused,
Into the mighty vision passing—there
As in her natural form, swell'd vast to Heaven !

Awake, my soul ! not only passive praise
Thou owest ! not alone these swelling tears,
Mute thanks and secret ecstasy !   Awake,
Voice of sweet song !   Awake, my heart, awake !
Green vales and icy cliffs, all join my Hymn. §

---

* Deep is the sky and black : transpicuous, deep.—1802.
† Form.—*Ib.*                ‡ Bodily eye—*ib.*
§ Yet thou, meantime, wast working on my soul,
  E'en like some deep enchanting melody,

Thou first and chief, sole sovran * of the Vale !
O struggling with the darkness all the night,†
And visited all night by troops of stars,
Or when they climb the sky or when they sink :
Companion of the morning-star at dawn,
Thyself Earth's rosy star, and of the dawn
Co-herald : wake, O wake, and utter praise !
Who sank thy sunless pillars deep in Earth ?
Who fill'd thy countenance with rosy light ?
Who made thee parent ‡ of perpetual streams ?

And you, ye five wild torrents fiercely glad !
Who call'd you forth from night and utter death,
From dark and icy caverns call'd you forth, §
Down those precipitous, black, jagged Rocks,

So sweet, we know not we are listening to it.
But I awake, and with a busier mind
And active will self-conscious, offer now
Not, as before, involuntary prayer
And passive adoration !

          Hand and voice,
Awake, awake ! and thou, my heart, awake !
Awake, ye rocks ! Ye forest pines, awake !
Green fields, and icy cliffs ! All join my hymn !
                      1802.

* In *The Friend* of November 16, 1809, are some corrections of this poem—for " sole sovran " we are told to read " *stern monarch.*"

† And thou, O silent mountain, sole and bare,
  O blacker than the darkness all the night—1802.

‡ Father—*ib.*

§ From darkness let you loose, and icy dens—*ib.*

For ever shatter'd and the same for ever?
Who gave you your invulnerable life,
Your strength, your speed, your fury, and your joy,
Unceasing thunder and eternal foam?
And who commanded (and the silence came,)
Here let the billows stiffen, and have rest?

Ye ice-falls! ye that from the mountain's brow
Adown enormous ravines slope amain—*
Torrents, methinks, that heard a mighty voice,
And stopp'd at once amid their maddest plunge!
Motionless torrents! silent cataracts!
Who made you glorious as the gates of Heaven
Beneath the keen full moon? Who bade the sun
Clothe you with rainbows? Who, with living
    flowers
Of loveliest blue,† spread garlands at your feet?—
God! let the torrents, like a shout of nations,
Answer! and let the ice-plains echo, God!‡
God! sing ye meadow-streams with gladsome
    voice!
Ye pine-groves, with your soft and soul-like sounds!
And they too have a voice, yon piles of snow,
And in their perilous fall shall thunder, God!§

---

* Ye that from yon dizzy heights
    Adown enormous ravines steeply slope—1802.

† Who with lovely flowers
    Of living blue, &c.—*ib.*

‡ God! God! the torrents, like a shout of nations,
    Utter! The ice-plain bursts, and answers God!—*ib.*

§ The silent snow-mass, loosening, thunders God!—*ib.*

Ye living flowers that skirt the eternal frost !
Ye wild goats sporting round the eagle's nest !
Ye eagles, play-mates of the mountain-storm ! *
Ye lightnings, the dread arrows of the clouds !
Ye signs and wonders of the element !
Utter forth God, and fill the hills with praise !

Thou too, hoar Mount ! † with thy sky-pointing
    peaks,
Oft from whose feet the avalanche, unheard,
Shoots downward, glittering through ‡ the pure
    serene
Into the depth of clouds, that veil thy breast—
Thou too again, stupendous Mountain ! thou
That as I raise my head, awhile § bow'd low
In adoration, upward from thy base
Slow travelling with dim eyes suffused with tears,
Solemnly seemest, like a vapoury cloud,
To rise before me—Rise, O ever rise,
Rise like a cloud of incense from the Earth !
Thou kingly Spirit throned among the hills,
Thou dread ambassador from Earth to Heaven,
Great hierarch ! tell thou the silent sky,
And tell the stars, and tell yon rising sun
Earth, with her thousand voices, praises God.

   \* Ye dreadless flowers, that fringe th' eternal frost !
     Ye wild goats, bounding by the eagle's nest !
     Ye eagles, playmates of the mountain blast !—1802.

   † The list of corrections already alluded to alters this to—
         " And thou, hoar Mount !"

   ‡ Glittering in—1809.

   § That as once more I raise my head—*ib.*

## THE BRITISH STRIPLING'S
## WAR-SONG.*

### IMITATED FROM STOLBERG.

YES, noble old Warrior! this heart has beat high,
    Since you told of the deeds which our coun-
        trymen wrought ;
O lend me the sabre that hung by thy thigh
    And I too will fight as my forefathers fought.

Despise not my youth, for my spirit is steel'd
    And I know there is strength in the grasp of my
        hand ;
Yea, as firm as thyself would I march to the field,
    And as proudly would die for my dear native
        land.

In the sports of my childhood I mimick'd the fight,
    The sound of a trumpet suspended my breath ;
And my fancy still wander'd by day and by night,
    Amid battle and tumult, 'mid conquest and death.

My own shout of onset, when the Armies advance,
    How oft it awakes me from visions of glory ;
When I meant to have leapt on the Hero of France,
    And have dash'd him to earth, pale and breath-
        less and gory.

* *Morning Post*, August 24, 1799 ; *Annual Anthology*,
1800, signed " Esteesi."

As late thro' the city with banners all streaming
  To the music of trumpets the Warriors flew by,
With helmet and scimitars naked and gleaming,
    On their proud-trampling, thunder-hoof'd steeds
      did they fly ;

I sped to yon heath that is lonely and bare,
  For each nerve was unquiet, each pulse in alarm ;
And I hurl'd the mock-lance thro' the objectless
      air,
    And in open-eyed dream proved the strength of
      my arm.

Yes, noble old Warrior ! this heart has beat high,
  Since you told of the deeds that our countrymen
      wrought ;
O lend me the sabre that hung by thy thigh,
    And I too will fight as my forefathers fought ! *

## LINES

### WRITTEN IN THE ALBUM AT ELBINGERODE, IN THE HARTZ FOREST.†

I STOOD on Brocken's ‡ sovran height, and saw
  Woods crowding upon woods, hills over hills,

* This poem is reprinted in Coleridge's *Literary Remains*
(vol. i. pp. 276-77), with a few unimportant verbal variations.

† Printed in *The Morning Post*, September 17, 1799, and in
*The Annual Anthology*, vol. ii., Bristol, 1800.

‡ The highest mountain in the Hartz, and indeed in North
Germany.

A surging scene, and only limited
By the blue distance.   Heavily my way
Downward I dragg'd through fir-groves evermore,
Where bright green moss heaves in sepulchral forms
Speckled with sunshine ; and, but seldom heard,
The sweet bird's song became a hollow sound ;
And the breeze, murmuring indivisibly,
Preserved its solemn murmur most distinct
From many a note of many a waterfall,
And the brook's chatter ; 'mid whose islet-stones
The dingy kidling with its tinkling bell
Leap'd frolicsome, or old romantic goat
Sat, his white beard slow waving.   I moved on
In low and languid mood : for I had found
That outward forms, the loftiest, still receive
Their finer influence from the Life within ;—
Fair cyphers else : fair, but of import vague
Or unconcerning, where the heart not finds *
History or prophecy of friend, or child,†
Or gentle maid, our first and early love,
Or father, or the venerable name
Of our adored country !   O thou Queen,
Thou delegated Deity of Earth,

---

  * Fair cyphers of vague import, where the eye
      Traces no spot, in which the heart may read, &c.
                                                    1817.

  †                   For I had found
      That grandest scenes have but imperfect charms,
      Where the sight vainly wanders, nor beholds
      One spot with which the heart associates
      Holy remembrances of friend or child, &c.—1799.

O dear, dear England ! how my longing eye
Turn'd westward, shaping in the steady clouds
Thy sands and high white cliffs !

     My native Land !
Fill'd with the thought of thee this heart was proud,
Yea, mine eye swam with tears : that all the view
From sovran Brocken, woods and woody hills,
Floated away, like a departing dream,
Feeble and dim ! Stranger, these impulses
Blame thou not lightly ; nor will I profane,
With hasty judgment or injurious doubt,
That man's sublimer spirit, who can feel
That God is everywhere ! the God who framed
Mankind to be one mighty family,
Himself our Father, and the World our Home.


## INSCRIPTION FOR A FOUNTAIN
## ON A HEATH.*

THIS Sycamore, oft musical with bees,—
  Such tents the Patriarchs loved !—O long
   unharm'd
May all its aged boughs † o'er-canopy
The small round basin, which this jutting stone
Keeps pure from falling leaves ! Long may the
  Spring,

 * Printed in *The Morning Post*, September 24, 1802, with
the title " Inscription on a Jutting Stone over a Spring."
 † Darksome boughs—1802.

Quietly as a sleeping infant's breath,
Send up cold waters to the traveller
With soft and even pulse !   Nor ever cease
Yon tiny cone of sand its soundless * dance,
Which at the bottom, like a Fairy's page,
As merry and no taller, dances still,
Nor wrinkles the smooth surface of the Fount.
Here twilight is and coolness : here is moss,
A soft seat, and a deep and ample shade.
Thou may'st toil far and find no second tree.
Drink, Pilgrim, here ! † here rest ! and if thy heart
Be innocent, here too shalt thou refresh
Thy Spirit, listening to some gentle sound,
Or passing gale or hum of murmuring bees ! ‡


## A TOMBLESS EPITAPH. §

TIS true, Idoloclastes Satyrane !
    (So call him, for so mingling blame with praise
And smiles with anxious looks, his earliest friends,
Masking his birth-name, wont to character

---

* Noiseless dance—1802.     † Here, stranger, drink!—*ib.*

‡ The passing gale or ever murmuring bees.—*Ib.*

§ First printed (without a title) in *The Friend* of November 23, 1809, with the following note :—" Imitated, though in the movements rather than the thoughts, from the seventh of *Gli Epitafi* of Chiabrera,
          " Fu ver che Ambrosio Salinero a torto
            Si pose in pena d' odiose liti," &c.

His wild-wood fancy and impetuous zeal)
Tis true that, passionate for ancient truths,
And honouring with religious love the great
Of elder times, he hated to excess,
With an unquiet and intolerant scorn,
The hollow puppets of a hollow age,
Ever idolatrous, and changing ever
Its worthless idols ! learning, power, and time,
(Too much of all) thus wasting in vain war
Of fervid colloquy.   Sickness, 'tis true,
Whole years of weary days, besieged him close,
Even to the gates and inlets of his life !
But it is true, no less, that strenuous, firm,
And with a natural gladness, he maintain'd
The citadel unconquer'd, and in joy
Was strong to follow the delightful Muse.
For not a hidden path, that to the shades
Of the beloved Parnassian forest leads,
Lurk'd undiscover'd by him ; not a rill
There issues from the fount of Hippocrene,
But he had traced it upward to its source,
Through open glade, dark glen, and secret dell,
Knew the gay wild flowers on its banks, and cull'd
Its medicinable herbs.   Yea, oft alone,
Piercing the long-neglected holy cave,
The haunt obscure of old Philosophy,
He bade with lifted torch its starry walls
Sparkle, as erst they sparkled to the flame
Of odorous lamps tended by Saint and Sage.
O framed for calmer times and nobler hearts !
O studious Poet, eloquent for truth !

Philosopher ! contemning wealth and death,
Yet docile, childlike, full of Life * and Love !
Here, rather than on monumental stone,
This record of thy worth thy Friend inscribes,
Thoughtful, with quiet tears upon his cheek.

## THIS LIME-TREE BOWER MY PRISON. †

### ADDRESSED TO CHARLES LAMB, OF THE INDIA HOUSE, LONDON.

In the June of 1797 some long-expected friends
paid a visit to the author's cottage ; and on the morning of their arrival, he met with an accident, which
disabled him from walking during the whole time of
their stay. One evening, when they had left him for
a few hours, he composed the following lines in the
garden-bower.

WELL, they are gone, and here must I remain,
  This lime-tree bower my prison ! I have lost
Beauties and feelings, such as would have been ‡
Most sweet to my remembrance even when age
Had dimm'd mine eyes to blindness ! They,
  meanwhile,
Friends, whom I never more may meet again, §

---

 * Light—1809.

 † Printed in *The Annual Anthology*, Bristol, vol. ii., 1800.

 ‡ Such beauties and such feelings as had been—1817.

 § My friends, whom I shall never meet again—*ib.*

On springy heath, along the hill-top edge,
Wander in gladness, and wind down, perchance,
To that still roaring dell, of which I told ;
The roaring dell, o'erwooded, narrow, deep,
And only speckled by the mid-day sun ;
Where its slim trunk the ash from rock to rock
Flings arching like a bridge ;—that branchless ash,
Unsunn'd and damp, whose few poor yellow leaves
Ne'er tremble in the gale, yet tremble still,
Fann'd by the water-fall ! and there my friends
Behold the dark green file of long lank weeds,*
That all at once (a most fantastic sight !)
Still nod and drip beneath the dripping edge
Of the blue clay-stone.

           Now my friends emerge
Beneath the wide wide Heaven—and view again
The many-steepled tract magnificent
Of hilly fields and meadows, and the sea,
With some fair bark, perhaps, whose sails light up
The slip of smooth clear blue betwixt two Isles
Of purple shadow ! Yes ! they wander on
In gladness all ; but thou, methinks, most glad,
My gentle-hearted Charles ! † for thou hast pined

---

* *Of long lank weeds.*] The *Asplenium Scolopendrium*,
called in some countries the Adder's Tongue, in others the
Hart's Tongue : but Withering gives the Adder's Tongue as
the trivial name of the *Ophioglossum* only.

  † " In the next edition of the *Anthology*, please to blot out
' gentle-hearted,' and substitute drunken-dog, ragged-head,

And hunger'd after Nature, many a year,
In the great City pent, winning thy way
With sad yet patient soul, through evil and pain
And strange calamity !   Ah ! slowly sink
Behind the western ridge, thou glorious Sun !
Shine in the slant beams of the sinking orb,
Ye purple heath-flowers ! richlier burn, ye clouds !
Live in the yellow light, ye distant groves !
And kindle, thou blue Ocean !   So my friend
Struck with deep joy may stand, as I have stood,
Silent with swimming sense ; yea, gazing round
On the wide landscape, gaze till all doth seem
Less gross than bodily ; [a living thing
Which acts upon the mind] and of such hues
As veil* the Almighty Spirit, when yet he makes
Spirits perceive his presence.

     A delight
Comes sudden on my heart, and I am glad
As I myself were there !   Nor in this bower,

---

seld-shaven, odd-eyed, stuttering, or any other epithet which
truly and properly belongs to the gentleman in question. And
for Charles read Tom, or Bob, or Richard, for mere delicacy.
. . . .  For God's sake (I never was more serious) don't
make me ridiculous any more by terming me "gentle-hearted"
in print, or do it in better verses.  Besides that the meaning of
gentle is equivocal at best, and almost always means poor-
spirited, the very quality of gentleness is abhorrent to such vile
trumpetings.  My *sentiment* is long since vanished.  I hope
my *virtues* have done *sucking*."—LAMB TO COLERIDGE.

   *    With such hues
  As clothe, &c.—1817.

This little lime-tree bower, have I not mark'd
Much that has soothed me.   Pale beneath the
    blaze
Hung the transparent foliage ; and I watch'd
Some broad and sunny leaf, and loved to see
The shadow of the leaf and stem above
Dappling its sunshine !   And that walnut-tree
Was richly tinged, and a deep radiance lay
Full on the ancient ivy, which usurps
Those fronting elms, and now, with blackest mass
Makes their dark branches gleam a lighter hue
Through the late twilight : and though now the bat
Wheels silent by, and not a swallow twitters,
Yet still the solitary humble bee
Sings in the bean-flower ! Henceforth I shall know
That Nature ne'er deserts the wise and pure ;
No plot so narrow, be but Nature there,
No waste so vacant, but may well employ
Each faculty of sense, and keep the heart
Awake to Love and Beauty ! and sometimes
'Tis well to be bereft of promised good,
That we may lift the soul, and contemplate
With lively joy the joys we cannot share.
My gentle-hearted Charles ! when the last rook
Beat its straight path along the dusky air
Homewards, I blest it ! deeming, its black wing
(Now a dim speck, now vanishing in light)
Had cross'd the mighty orb's dilated glory,
While thou stood'st gazing ; or when all was still,

\* Flew creeking o'er thy head, and had a charm
For thee, my gentle-hearted Charles, to whom
No sound is dissonant which tells of Life.


## ODE TO GEORGIANA, DUCHESS
## OF DEVONSHIRE,

### ON THE TWENTY-FOURTH STANZA IN HER "PASSAGE OVER MOUNT GOTHARD." †

" And hail the Chapel ! hail the Platform wild!
    Where Tell directed the avenging dart,
With well-strung arm, that first preserved his child,
    Then aim'd the arrow at the tyrant's heart."

### I.

SPLENDOUR'S fondly-foster'd child ! ‡
    And did you hail the platform wild,
Where once the Austrian fell
Beneath the shaft of Tell !
O Lady, nursed in pomp and pleasure !
Whence learnt you that heroic measure ?

---

\* *Flew creeking.*]   Some months after I had written this
line, it gave me pleasure to find that Bartram had observed
the same circumstance of the Savanna Crane.   " When these
Birds move their wings in flight, their strokes are slow, mode-
rate and regular ; and even when at a considerable distance
or high above us, we plainly hear the quill-feathers ; their
shafts and webs upon one another creek as the joints or working of a vessel in a tempestuous sea.

    † Printed in the *Morning Post*, December 24, 1799.

    ‡ Lady, Splendour's foster'd child !—1799.

## II.

Light as a dream your days their circlets * ran,
From all that teaches brotherhood to Man
Far, far removed! from want, from hope, from fear!
Enchanting music lull'd your infant ear,
Obeisance, praises † soothed your infant heart:
  Emblazonments and old ancestral crests,
With many a bright obtrusive form of art,
Detain'd your eye from Nature: stately vests, ‡
That veiling strove to deck your charms divine,
Rich viands and the pleasurable wine,
Were yours unearn'd by toil; nor could you see
The unenjoying toiler's misery.
And yet, free Nature's uncorrupted child,
You hail'd the Chapel and the Platform wild,
    Where once the Austrian fell
    Beneath the shaft of Tell!
  O Lady, nursed in pomp and pleasure!
  Whence learnt you that heroic measure?

## III.

There crowd your finely-fibred frame
  All living faculties of bliss;
And Genius to your cradle came,
His forehead wreathed with lambent flame,
  And bending low, with godlike kiss
  Breathed in a more celestial life;
But boasts not many a fair compeer

* Courses—1799.    † Obeisant praises—1817.
‡ Gorgeous vests—*ib.*

A heart as sensitive to joy and fear? *
And some, perchance, might wage an equal strife,
Some few, to nobler being wrought,
Co-rivals in the nobler gift of thought. †
    Yet these delight to celebrate
    Laurell'd War and plumy State;
    Or in verse and music dress
    Tales of rustic happiness—
Pernicious tales! insidious strains!
    That steel the rich man's breast,
    And mock the lot unblest,
The sordid vices and the abject pains,
Which evermore must be
The doom of ignorance and penury! ‡
But you, free Nature's uncorrupted child,
You hail'd the Chapel § and the Platform wild,
    Where once the Austrian fell
    Beneath the shaft of Tell!
O Lady, nursed in pomp and pleasure!
Whence learnt you that heroic measure?

### IV.

You were a mother! That most holy name,
    Which Heaven and Nature bless,
I may not vilely prostitute to those
    Whose infants owe them less

---

\* But many of thy many fair compeers
  Have frames as sensible of joys and fears :—1799.

† The plastic powers of thought.—*Ib.*

‡ Poverty—*ib.*

§ Hail'd the low Chapel, &c.—*ib.*

Than the poor caterpillar owes *
   Its gaudy parent fly.
You were a mother ! at your bosom fed
  The babes that loved you.   You, with laughing
     eye,
Each twilight-thought, each nascent feeling read,
  Which you yourself created.   Oh ! delight !
    A second time to be a mother,
      Without the mother's bitter groans :
    Another thought, and yet another,
      By touch, or taste, by looks or tones,
   O'er the growing sense to roll,
   The mother of your infant's soul !
The Angel of the Earth, who, while he guides
  His chariot-planet round the goal of day,
All trembling gazes on the eye of God,
  A moment turn'd his awful face away ;
And as he view'd you, from his aspect sweet
  New influences in your being rose,
Blest intuitions and communions fleet
  With living Nature, in her joys and woes !
    Thenceforth your soul rejoiced to see †
    The shrine of social Liberty !
    O beautiful ! O Nature's child !
    'Twas thence you hail'd the Platform wild,
      Where once the Austrian fell
      Beneath the shaft of Tell !
    O Lady, nursed in pomp and pleasure !
    Thence learnt you that heroic measure.

---

* Than the poor reptile owes—1799.
† O Lady ! thence you joy'd to see—*ib.*

## TRANQUILLITY :* AN ODE.

*Vix ea nostra voco.*

WHAT statesmen scheme and soldiers
　　　work,
Whether the Pontiff or the Turk
Will e'er renew th'expiring lease
Of empire ; whether war or peace
Will best play off the Consul's game ;
What fancy-figures, and what name
Half-thinking sensual France, a natural slave,
On those ne'er broken chains, her self-forged chains,
　　will grave ;

Disturb not me ! Some tears I shed
When bow'd the Swiss his noble head ;
Since then, with quiet heart have view'd
Both distant fights and treaties crude,
Whose heap'd-up terms, which fear compels,
(Live Discord's green combustibles,
And future fuel of the funeral pyre)
Now hide, and soon, alas ! will feed the low-burnt
　　fire.]

Tranquillity ! thou better name
Than all the family of Fame !
Thou ne'er wilt leave my riper age
To low intrigue, or factious rage ;
For oh ! dear child of thoughtful Truth,

* Printed in the *Morning Post*, Dec. 4, 1801. Reprinted
without the first two stanzas in the first number of *The Friend*,
1809.

To thee I gave my early youth,
And left the bark, and blest the steadfast shore,
Ere yet the tempest * rose and scared me with its
  roar.

Who late and lingering seeks thy shrine,
 On him but seldom, Power divine,
  Thy spirit rests ! Satiety
 And Sloth, poor counterfeits of thee,
 Mock the tired worldling. Idle Hope
 And dire Remembrance interlope,
To vex the feverish slumbers of the mind :
The bubble floats before, the spectre stalks behind.

But me thy gentle hand will lead †
 At morning through the accustom'd mead ;
 And in the sultry summer's heat
 Will build me up a mossy seat ;
 And when the gust of Autumn crowds,
 And breaks the busy moonlight clouds,
Thou best the thought canst raise,‡ the heart attune,
Light as the busy clouds, calm as the gliding moon.

The feeling heart, the searching soul,
 To thee I dedicate the whole !
 And while within myself I trace
 The greatness of some future race,
 Aloof with hermit-eye I scan
 The present works of present man—
A wild and dream-like trade of blood and guile,
Too foolish for a tear, too wicked for a smile !

* The storm-wind—1801. † The Power divine will lead—*ib.*
‡ She best the thought will lift—*ib.*

## DEJECTION: AN ODE.*

### WRITTEN APRIL 4, 1802.

> Late, late yestreen I saw the new Moon,
> With the old Moon in her arms;
> And I fear, I fear, my Master dear!
> We shall have a deadly storm.
>
> BALLAD OF SIR PATRICK SPENCE.

### I.

WELL! If the Bard was weather-wise, who made
  The grand old ballad of Sir Patrick Spence,
This night, so tranquil now, will not go hence
Unroused by winds, that ply a busier trade
Than those which mould yon cloud in lazy flakes,
Or the dull sobbing draft, that moans and rakes
  Upon the strings of this Eolian lute,
   Which better far were mute.
For lo! the New-moon winter-bright!
And overspread with phantom light,
(With swimming phantom light o'erspread
But rimm'd and circled by a silver thread)
I see the old Moon in her lap, foretelling
  The coming-on of rain and squally blast.
And oh! that even now the gust were swelling,
  And the slant night-shower driving loud and fast!

---

\* Printed in *The Morning Post*, Oct. 4, 1802. The poem in its original form is addressed to "Edmund," not, as in the later version, to a "lady."

Those sounds which oft have raised me, whilst they
    And sent my soul abroad,        [awed,
Might now perhaps their wonted impulse give,
Might startle this dull pain, and make it move and
     live !

### II.

A grief without a pang, void, dark, and drear,
  A stifled, drowsy, unimpassion'd grief,
  Which finds no natural outlet, no relief,
    In word, or sigh, or tear—
O Lady ! in this wan and heartless mood,
To other thoughts by yonder throstle woo'd,
  All this long eve, so balmy and serene,
Have I been gazing on the western sky,
  And its peculiar tint of yellow green :
And still I gaze—and with how blank an eye !
And those thin clouds above, in flakes and bars,
That give away their motion to the stars ;
Those stars, that glide behind them or between,
Now sparkling, now bedimm'd, but always seen :
Yon crescent Moon, as fix'd as if it grew
In its own cloudless, starless lake of blue ;
[A boat becalm'd ! a lovely sky-canoe !]
I see them all so excellently fair,
I *see*, not *feel*, how beautiful they are !

### III.

    My genial spirits fail ;
    And what can these avail
To lift the smothering weight from off my breast ?
    It were a vain endeavour,
    Though I should gaze for ever

On that green light that lingers in the west :
I may not hope from outward forms to win
The passion and the life, whose fountains are within.

### IV.

O Lady ! we receive but what we give,
And in *our* life alone does Nature live :
Ours is her wedding-garment, ours her shroud !
   And would we aught behold, of higher worth,
Than that inanimate cold world allow'd
To the poor loveless ever-anxious crowd,
   Ah ! from the soul itself must issue forth
A light, a glory, a fair luminous cloud
     Enveloping the Earth—
And from the soul itself must there be sent
   A sweet and potent voice, of its own birth,
Of all sweet sounds the life and element !

### V.

O pure of heart ! thou need'st not ask of me
What this strong music in the soul may be !
What, and wherein it doth exist,
This light, this glory, this fair luminous mist,
This beautiful and beauty-making power.
   Joy, virtuous Lady ! Joy that ne'er was given,
Save to the pure, and in their purest hour,
Life, and Life's effluence, cloud at once and shower,
Joy, Lady ! is the spirit and the power,
Which wedding Nature to us gives in dower,
   A new Earth and new Heaven,
Undreamt of by the sensual and the proud—

Joy is the sweet voice, Joy the luminous cloud—
  We in ourselves rejoice !
And thence flows all that charms or ear or sight,
 All melodies the echoes of that voice,
All colours a suffusion from that light.

### VI.*

There was a time when, though my path was rough,
 This joy within me dallied with distress,
And all misfortunes were but as the stuff
 Whence Fancy made me dreams of happiness :
For hope grew round me, like the twining vine,
And fruits, and foliage, not my own, seem'd mine.
But now afflictions bow me down to earth :
Nor care I that they rob me of my mirth ;
  But oh ! each visitation
Suspends what Nature gave me at my birth,
 My shaping spirit of Imagination.
For not to think of what I needs must feel,
 But to be still and patient, all I can ;
And haply by abstruse research to steal
 From my own nature all the natural man—
 This was my sole resource, my only plan :
Till that which suits a part infects the whole,
And now is almost grown the habit of my soul.

### VII.

Hence, viper thoughts, that coil around my mind,
  Reality's dark dream !

* This stanza originally began :—
   " Yes, dearest Edmund, yes ! "

I turn from you, and listen to the wind,*
 Which long has raved unnoticed.  What a scream
Of agony by torture lengthen'd out
That lute sent forth !   Thou Wind, that ravest
  without,
 Bare crag, or mountain-tairn,† or blasted tree,
Or pine-grove whither woodman never clomb,
Or lonely house, long held the witches' home,
 Methinks were fitter instruments for thee,
Mad Lutanist ! who in this month of showers,
Of dark-brown gardens, and of peeping flowers,
Makest Devils' yule, with worse than wintry song,
The blossoms, buds, and timorous leaves among.
 Thou Actor, perfect in all tragic sounds !
Thou mighty Poet, even to frenzy bold !
  What tell'st thou now about?
 'Tis of the rushing of a host in rout,
 With groans of trampled men,‡ with smarting
  wounds—
At once they groan with pain, and shudder with
  the cold !
But hush ! there is a pause of deepest silence !

* O wherefore did I let it haunt my mind,
  This dark distressful dream ?
 I turn from it, and listen to the wind—1802.

 † Tairn is a small lake, generally if not always applied to
the lakes up in the mountains, and which are the feeders of
those in the valleys.   This address to the Storm-wind will not
appear extravagant to those who have heard it at night, and
in a mountainous country.

 ‡ With many groans of men—1802.

And all that noise, as of a rushing crowd,
With groans, and tremulous shudderings—all is
  over—
 It tells another tale, with sounds less deep and
  A tale of less affright,     [loud !
  And temper'd with delight,
As Otway's self had framed the tender lay,
  'Tis of a little child
  Upon a lonesome wild,
Not far from home, but she hath lost her way :
And now moans low in bitter grief and fear,
And now screams loud, and hopes to make her
  mother hear.

### VIII.

'Tis midnight, but small thoughts have I of sleep :
Full seldom may my friend such vigils keep !
Visit her, gentle Sleep ! with wings of healing,
 And may this storm be but a mountain-birth,
May all the stars hang bright above her dwelling,
 Silent as though they watch'd the sleeping Earth.
  With light heart may she rise,
  Gay fancy, cheerful eyes,*
Joy lift her spirit, joy attune her voice ;

---

 * Here followed in the original version these lines :

  " And sing his lofty song, and teach me to rejoice !
   O Edmund, friend of my devoutest choice,
   O raised from anxious dread and busy care
   By the immenseness of the good and fair
   Which thou seest every where,
   Joy lifts thy spirit, joy attunes," &c.—1802.

To her may all things live, from pole to pole,
Their life the eddying of her living soul !
    O simple spirit, guided from above,
Dear Lady ! friend devoutest of my choice,
Thus may'st thou ever, evermore rejoice.


## TO A FRIEND

### WHO HAD DECLARED HIS INTENTION OF WRITING NO MORE POETRY.*

DEAR Charles ! whilst yet thou wert a babe, I
      ween
That Genius plunged thee in that wizard fount
Hight Castalie : and (sureties of thy faith)
That Pity and Simplicity stood by,
And promised for thee, that thou shouldst renounce
The world's low cares and lying vanities,
Steadfast and rooted in the heavenly Muse,
And wash'd and sanctified to Poesy.
Yes—thou wert plunged, but with forgetful hand
Held, as by Thetis erst her warrior son :
And with those recreant unbaptized heels
Thou'rt flying from thy bounden ministeries—
So sore it seems and burthensome a task
To weave unwithering flowers ! But take thou heed :
For thou art vulnerable, wild-eyed boy,
And I have arrows† mystically dipt,

---

* Printed in *The Annual Anthology*, Bristol, vol. ii. (1800).
† Pind. Olymp, ii. 1. 156.

Such as may stop thy speed.   Is thy Burns dead?
And shall he die unwept, and sink to earth
" Without the meed of one melodious tear ?"
Thy Burns, and Nature's own beloved bard,
Who to the " Illustrious* of his native Land
So properly did look for patronage."
Ghost of Mæcenas ! hide thy blushing face !
They snatch'd him from the sickle and the plough—
To gauge ale-firkins.

                  Oh ! for shame return !
On a bleak rock, midway the Aonian mount,
There stands a lone and melancholy tree,
Whose aged branches to the midnight blast
Make solemn music : pluck its darkest bough,
Ere yet the unwholesome night-dew be exhaled,
And weeping wreath it round thy Poet's tomb.
Then in the outskirts, where pollutions grow,
Pick the rank henbane and the dusky flowers
Of night-shade, or its red and tempting fruit,
These with stopp'd nostril and glove-guarded hand
Knit in nice intertexture, so to twine,
The illustrious brow of Scotch Nobility !
  1796.

---

  * Verbatim from Burns' Dedication of his Poems to the
Nobility and Gentry of the Caledonian Hunt.

## TO WILLIAM WORDSWORTH.

COMPOSED ON THE NIGHT AFTER HIS RECITATION
OF A POEM ON THE GROWTH OF AN
INDIVIDUAL MIND.*

FRIEND of the wise ! and teacher of the good !
    Into my heart have I received that lay
More than historic, that prophetic lay
Wherein (high theme by thee first sung aright)
Of the foundations and the building up
Of a Human Spirit thou hast dared to tell
What may be told, to the understanding mind
Revealable ; and what within the mind
By vital breathings secret as the soul †
Of vernal growth, oft quickens in the heart
Thoughts all too deep for words !—·

              Theme hard as high
Of smiles spontaneous, and mysterious fears
(The first-born they of Reason and twin-birth),
Of tides obedient to external force,
And currents self-determined, as might seem,
Or by some inner Power ; of moments awful,
Now in thy inner life, and now abroad,
When power stream'd from thee, and thy soul
      received

* *The Prelude*, commenced in the beginning of 1799 and
completed in May, 1805, was read by Wordsworth to Coleridge after the return of the latter from Malta. This poem
was not published until after the author's death in 1850.—ED.

† Like the secret soul—1817.

The light reflected, as a light bestow'd—
Of fancies fair, and milder hours of youth,
Hyblean murmurs of poetic thought
Industrious in its joy, in vales and glens
Native or outland, lakes and famous hills !
Or on the lonely high-road, when the stars
Were rising ; or by secret mountain-streams,
The guides and the companions of thy way !

Of more than Fancy, of the Social Sense
Distending wide, and man beloved as man,
Where France in all her towns lay vibrating
Like some becalmed bark* beneath the burst
Of Heaven's immediate thunder, when no cloud
Is visible, or shadow on the main.
For thou wert there, thine own brows garlanded,
Amid the tremor of a realm aglow,
Amid a mighty nation jubilant,
When from the general heart of human kind
Hope sprang forth like a full-born Deity !
——Of that dear Hope afflicted and struck down,
So summon'd homeward, thenceforth calm and sure
From the dread watch-tower of man's absolute self,
With light unwaning on her eyes, to look
Far on—herself a glory to behold,
The Angel of the vision ! Then (last strain)
Of Duty, chosen laws controlling choice,
Action and joy !—An Orphic song indeed,

* Even as a bark becalm'd—1817.

A song divine of high and passionate thoughts
To their own music chanted !

                              O great Bard !
Ere yet that last strain dying awed the air,
With steadfast eye I view'd thee in the choir
Of ever-enduring men.   The truly great
Have all one age, and from one visible space
Shed influence ! They, both in power and act,
Are permanent, and Time is not with them,
Save as it worketh for them, they in it.
Nor less a sacred roll, than those of old,
And to be placed, as they, with gradual fame
Among the archives of mankind, thy work
Makes audible a linked lay of Truth,
Of Truth profound a sweet continuous lay,
Not learnt, but native, her own natural notes !
Ah ! as I listen'd with a heart forlorn,
The pulses of my being beat anew :
And even as life returns upon the drown'd,
Life's joy rekindling roused a throng of pains—
Keen pangs of Love, awakening as a babe
Turbulent, with an outcry in the heart ;
And fears self-will'd, that shunn'd the eye of hope ;
And hope that scarce would know itself from fear ;
Sense of past youth, and manhood come in vain,
And genius given, and knowledge won in vain ;
And all which I had cull'd in wood-walks wild,
And all which patient toil had rear'd, and all,
Commune with thee had open'd out—but flowers
Strew'd on my corse, and borne upon my bier,
In the same coffin, for the self-same grave !

That way no more! and ill beseems it me,
Who came a welcomer in herald's guise,
Singing of glory, and futurity,
To wander back on such unhealthful road,
Plucking the poisons of self-harm! And ill
Such intertwine beseems triumphal wreaths
Strew'd before thy advancing!

                      Nor do thou,
Sage Bard! impair the memory of that hour
Of thy communion with my nobler mind
By pity or grief, already felt too long!
Nor let my words import more blame than needs.
The tumult rose and ceased: for peace is nigh
Where wisdom's voice has found a listening heart.
Amid the howl of more than wintry storms,
The halcyon hears the voice of vernal hours
Already on the wing.

                  Eve following eve,
Dear tranquil time, when the sweet sense of Home
Is sweetest! moments for their own sake hail'd
And more desired, more precious, for thy song,
In silence listening, like a devout child,
My soul lay passive, by thy various strain
Driven as in surges now beneath the stars,
With momentary stars of my own birth,
Fair constellated foam, still darting off
Into the darkness; now a tranquil sea,
Outspread and bright, yet swelling to the moon.

And when—O Friend! my comforter and guide!
Strong in thyself, and powerful to give strength!—

Thy long sustained Song finally closed,
And thy deep voice had ceased—yet thou thyself
Wert still before my eyes, and round us both
That happy vision of beloved faces—
Scarce conscious, and yet conscious of its close
I sate, my being blended in one thought
(Thought was it? or aspiration? or resolve?)
Absorb'd, yet hanging still upon the sound—
And when I rose, I found myself in prayer.

## A CHRISTMAS CAROL.*

### I.

THE shepherds went their hasty way,
　　And found the lowly stable-shed
Where the Virgin-Mother lay:
　　And now they check'd their eager tread,
For to the Babe, that at her bosom clung,
A mother's song the Virgin-Mother sung.

### II.

They told her how a glorious light,
　　Streaming from a heavenly throng,
Around them shone, suspending night!
　　While sweeter than a mother's song,
Blest Angels heralded the Saviour's birth,
Glory to God on high! and Peace on Earth.

### III.

She listen'd to the tale divine,
　　And closer still the Babe she prest;

* *Morning Post*, December 25, 1799.

And while she cried, the Babe is mine !
   The milk rush'd faster to her breast :
Joy rose within her, like a summer's morn ;
Peace, Peace on Earth ! the Prince of Peace is
     born.

### IV.

Thou Mother of the Prince of Peace,
   Poor, simple, and of low estate !
That strife should vanish, battle cease,
   O why should this thy soul elate ?
Sweet music's loudest note, the poet's story,—
Didst thou ne'er love to hear of fame and glory ?

### V.

And is not War a youthful king,
   A stately hero clad in mail ?
Beneath his footsteps laurels spring ;
   Him Earth's majestic monarchs hail
Their friend, their playmate ! and his bold bright
     eye
Compels the maiden's love-confessing sigh.

### VI.

" Tell this in some more courtly scene,
   To maids and youths in robes of state !
I am a woman poor and mean,
   And therefore is my soul elate.
War is a ruffian, all with guilt defiled,*
That from the aged father tears his child !

---

* A ruffian thief with gore defiled—1799.

### VII.

" A murderous fiend, * by fiends adored,
　　He kills the sire and starves the son ;
The husband kills, and from her board
　　Steals all his widow's toil had won ;
Plunders God's world of beauty ; rends away
All safety from the night, all comfort from the day.

### VIII.

" Then wisely is my soul elate,
　　That strife should vanish, battle cease :
I'm poor and of a low estate,
　　The Mother of the Prince of Peace.
Joy rises in me, like a summer's morn :
Peace, Peace on Earth ! the Prince of Peace is
　　born."

### [IX.

Strange prophecy ! could half the screams
　　Of half the men that since have died
To realize War's kingly dreams
　　Have risen at once in one vast tide,
The choral music of Heaven's multitude
Had been o'erpower'd and lost amid the uproar
　　rude !]

## THE VIRGIN'S CRADLE-HYMN.†

[About thirteen years ago or more, travelling
through the middle parts of Germany, I saw a little
print of the Virgin and Child in the small public-house

---

* Thief.—1799.　　　　† *Courier*, August 30, 1811.

of a Catholic village with the following beautiful Latin lines under it, which I transcribed. They may be easily adapted to the air of the famous Sicilian Hymn, *Adeste fideles, læti triumphantes*, by the omission of a few notes.]

DORMI, Jesu! Mater ridet
    Quæ tam dulcem somnum videt,
  Dormi, Jesu! blandule!
Si non dormis, Mater plorat,
Inter fila cantans orat,
  Blande, veni, somnule.

### ENGLISH.

Sleep, sweet babe! my cares beguiling:
Mother sits beside thee smiling;
  Sleep, my darling, tenderly!
If thou sleep not, mother mourneth,
Singing as her wheel she turneth:
  Come, soft slumber, balmily!

## TRANSLATION OF A PASSAGE

### IN OTTFRIED'S METRICAL PARAPHRASE OF THE GOSPEL.*

[This paraphrase, written about the time of Charlemagne, is by no means deficient in occasional passages of considerable poetic merit. There is a flow and a tender enthusiasm in the following lines which even in the translation will not, I flatter myself, fail to interest the reader. Ottfried is describing the circum-

---

* Printed in *Biographia Literaria*, London, 1817, i. 204.

stances immediately following the birth of our Lord.
Most interesting is it to consider the effect when the
feelings are wrought above the natural pitch by the
belief of something mysterious, while all the images
are purely natural. Then it is that religion and poetry
strike deepest.]

SHE gave with joy her virgin breast;
　　She hid it not, she bared the breast
Which suckled that divinest babe !
Blessed, blessed were the breasts
Which the Saviour infant kiss'd ;
And blessed was the mother
Who wrapp'd his limbs in swaddling clothes,
Singing placed him on her lap,
Hung o'er him with her looks of love,
And soothed him with a lulling motion.
Blessed ! for she shelter'd him
From the damp and chilling air ;
Blessed, blessed ! for she lay
With such a babe in one blest bed,
Close as babes and mothers lie !
Blessed, blessed evermore,
With her virgin lips she kiss'd,
With her arms, and to her breast,
She embraced the babe divine,
Her babe divine the virgin mother !
There lives not on this ring of earth
A mortal that can sing her praise.
Mighty mother, virgin pure,
In the darkness and the night
For us she *bore* the heavenly Lord !

## TO TWO SISTERS:

### A WANDERER'S FAREWELL.*

TO know, to esteem, to love,—and then to
    part—
Makes up life's tale to many a feeling heart;
Alas for some abiding-place of love,†
O'er which my spirit, like the mother dove,
Might brood with warming wings!

          O fair! O kind!
Sisters in blood, yet each with each intwined
More close by sisterhood of heart and mind! ‡
[Me disinherited in form and face
By nature, and mishap of outward grace;
Who, soul and body, through one guiltless fault
Waste daily with the poison of sad thought,
Me did you soothe, when solace hoped I none!
And as on unthaw'd ice the winter sun,
Though stern the frost, though brief the genial day,
You bless my heart with many a cheerful ray;
For gratitude suspends the heart's despair,
Reflecting bright though cold your image there.

* Printed in *The Courier*, December 10, 1807. A small
portion only of this poem, consisting of the opening and concluding lines, appeared in *Sibylline Leaves* headed " On
Taking Leave of ——."—ED.

  † O for some dear abiding-place of Love—1817.

  ‡            O fair as kind,
    Were but one sisterhood with you combined
    (Your very image they in shape and mind)—*Ib*.

Nay more ! its music by some sweeter strain
Makes us live o'er our happiest hours again,
Hope re-appearing dim in memory's guise—
Even thus did you call up before mine eyes
Two dear, dear Sisters, prized all price above,
Sisters, like you, with more than sisters' love ;
*So* like you *they*, and so in *you* were seen
Their relative statures, tempers, looks, and mien,
That oft, dear ladies ! you have been to me
At once a vision and reality.
Sight seem'd a sort of memory, and amaze
Mingled a trouble with affection's gaze.

Oft to my eager soul I whisper blame,
A Stranger bid it feel the Stranger's shame—
My eager soul, impatient of the name,
No strangeness owns, no Stranger's form descries :
The chidden heart spreads trembling on the eyes.
First-seen I gazed, as I would look you thro' !
My best-beloved regain'd their youth in you,—
And still I ask, though now familiar grown,
Are you for *their* sakes dear, or for your own ?

O doubly dear ! may Quiet with you dwell !
In Grief I love you, yet I love you well !
Hope long is dead to me ! an orphan's tear
Love wept despairing o'er his nurse's bier.
Yet still she flutters o'er her grave's green slope :
For Love's despair is but the ghost of Hope !

Sweet Sisters ! were you placed around one hearth
With those, your other selves in shape and worth,]

Far rather would I sit in solitude,
Fond recollections all my fond heart's food,*
And dream of *you*, sweet Sisters ! (ah ! not mine !)
And only *dream* of you (ah ! dream and pine !)
Than boast the presence † and partake the pride,
And shine in the eye, of all the world beside.

## FAREWELL TO LOVE.‡

FAREWELL, sweet Love ! yet blame you not
    my truth ;
  More fondly ne'er did mother eye her child
Than I your form : *yours* were my hopes of youth,
    And as *you* shaped my thoughts I sigh'd or
        smiled.

While most were wooing wealth, or gaily swerving
  To pleasure's secret haunts, and some apart
Stood strong in pride, self-conscious of deserving,
  To you I gave my whole weak wishing heart.

And when I met the maid that realized
  Your fair creations, and had won her kindness,
Say but for her if aught on earth I prized !
  *Your* dreams alone I dreamt, and caught your
      blindness.

* The forms of memory all my mental food—1817.

† Than have the presence—*Ib.*

‡ *Gentleman's Magazine*, November, 1815 ; *Literary Remains of S. T. C.*, vol. i. p. 280.

O grief !—but farewell, Love ! I will go play me
With thoughts that please me less and less betray
    me.

## THE BUTTERFLY.*

THE butterfly the ancient Grecians made
    The soul's fair emblem, and its only name †—
But of the soul, escaped the slavish trade
Of mortal life !—For in this earthly frame
Ours is the reptile's lot, much toil, much blame,
Manifold motions making little speed,
And to deform and kill the things whereon we feed.

## MUTUAL PASSION.

*Altered and modernized from an old Poet.* ‡

I LOVE, and he loves me again,
    Yet dare I not tell who :
For if the nymphs should know my swain,
    I fear they'd love him too.
      Yet while my joy's unknown,
      Its rosy buds are but half-blown :
What no one with me shares, seems scarce my own.

---

  * *Biographia Literaria*, London, 1817, vol. i. p. 82. *The Amulet*, 1833.

  † *Psyche* means both butterfly and soul.

  ‡ Printed in *The Courier*, September 21, 1811.

I'll tell, that if they be not glad,
    They yet may envy me :
But then if I grow jealous mad,
    And of them pitied be,
        'Twould vex me worse than scorn !
        And yet it cannot be forborne,
Unless my heart would like my thoughts be torn.

He is, if they can find him, fair
    And fresh, and fragrant too ;
As after rain the summer air,
    And looks as lilies do,
        That are this morning blown !
        Yet, yet I doubt, he is not known,
Yet, yet I fear to have him fully shown.

But he hath eyes so large, and bright,
    Which none can see, and doubt
That Love might thence his torches light
    Tho' Hate had put them out !
        But then to raise my fears,
        His voice——what maid soever hears
Will be my rival, though she have but ears.

I'll tell no more ! yet I love him,
    And he loves me ; yet so,
That never one low wish did dim
    Our love's pure light, I know——
        In each so free from blame,
        That both of us would gain new fame,
If love's strong fears would let me tell his name !

# THE THREE GRAVES.

## A FRAGMENT OF A SEXTON'S TALE.*

[THE Author has published the following humble fragment, encouraged by the decisive recommendation of
more than one of our most celebrated living Poets.
The language was intended to be dramatic; that is
suited to the narrator; and the metre corresponds to
the homeliness of the diction. It is therefore presented
as the fragment, not of a Poem, but of a common
Ballad-tale. Whether this is sufficient to justify the
adoption of such a style, in any metrical composition
not professedly ludicrous, the Author is himself in
some doubt. At all events, it is not presented as
poetry, and it is in no way connected with the
Author's judgment concerning poetic diction. Its
merits, if any, are exclusively psychological. The
story which must be supposed to have been narrated
in the first and second parts is as follows :—

Edward, a young farmer, meets at the house of
Ellen her bosom-friend Mary, and commences an
acquaintance, which ends in a mutual attachment.
With her consent, and by the advice of their common
friend Ellen, he announces his hopes and intentions
to Mary's mother, a widow-woman bordering on her
fortieth year, and from constant health, the possession

---

* First printed at the end of the sixth number of *The Friend*
(Thursday, September 21, 1809), as the third and fourth parts
of a tale consisting of six. "The two last parts," adds the
author, "may be given hereafter, if the present should appear
to have afforded pleasure, and to have answered the purpose
of a relief and amusement to my readers."

of a competent property, and from having had no other children but Mary and another daughter (the father died in their infancy), retaining for the greater part her personal attractions and comeliness of appearance; but a woman of low education and violent temper. The answer which she at once returned to Edward's application was remarkable—"Well, Edward! you are a handsome young fellow, and you shall have my daughter." From this time all their wooing passed under the mother's eyes; and, in fine, she became herself enamoured of her future son-in-law, and practised every art, both of endearment and of calumny, to transfer his affections from her daughter to herself. (The outlines of the Tale are positive facts, and of no very distant date, though the author has purposely altered the names and the scene of action, as well as invented the characters of the parties and the detail of the incidents.) Edward, however, though perplexed by her strange detractions from her daughter's good qualities, yet in the innocence of his own heart still mistaking her increasing fondness for motherly affection; she at length, overcome by her miserable passion, after much abuse of Mary's temper and moral tendencies, exclaimed with violent emotion—"O Edward! indeed, indeed, she is not fit for you—she has not a heart to love you as you deserve. It is I that love you! Marry me, Edward! and I will this very day settle all my property on you." The Lover's eyes were now opened; and thus taken by surprise, whether from the effect of the horror which he felt, acting as it were hysterically on his nervous system, or that at the first moment he lost the sense of the guilt of the proposal in the feeling of its strangeness and absurdity, he flung her from him and burst into a fit of laughter. Irritated by this almost to frenzy, the woman fell on her knees, and in a loud voice that approached to a scream, she prayed for a curse both on him and on her own child. Mary happened to be in the room directly above them, heard Edward's laugh, and her mother's blasphemous prayer, and fainted away. He, hearing the fall, ran up stairs, and taking her in his arms, carried her off to Ellen's home; and after some fruitless attempts on her part toward a reconciliation with her mother, she was married to him.—And here the third part of the Tale begins.

I was not led to choose this story from any partiality to tragic, much less to monstrous events (though at the time that I composed the verses, somewhat more than twelve years ago,* I was less averse to such subjects than at present), but from finding in it a striking proof of the possible effect on the imagination, from an idea violently and suddenly impressed on it. I had been reading Bryan Edwards's account of the effects of the Oby witchcraft on the Negroes in the West Indies, and Hearne's deeply interesting anecdotes of similar workings on the imagination of the Copper Indians (those of my readers who have it in their power will be well repaid for the trouble of referring to those works for the passages alluded to) ; and I conceived the design of showing that instances of this kind are not peculiar to savage or barbarous tribes, and of illustrating the mode in which the mind is affected in these cases, and the progress and symptoms of the morbid action on the fancy from the beginning.

* i. e. in 1797.—ED.

The Tale is supposed to be narrated by an old
Sexton, in a country church-yard, to a traveller
whose curiosity had been awakened by the appear
ance of three graves, close by each other, to two
only of which there were grave-stones. On the first
of these was the name, and dates, as usual : on the
second, no name, but only a date, and the words,
" The Mercy of God is infinite."]

1809.

THE grapes upon the Vicar's wall
    Were ripe as ripe could be ;*
And yellow leaves in sun and wind
    Were falling from the tree.

On the hedge-elms in the narrow lane
    Still swung the spikes of corn :
Dear Lord ! it seems but yesterday—
    Young Edward's marriage-morn.

Up through that wood behind the church,
    There leads from Edward's door
A mossy track, all over bough'd,
    For half a mile or more.

And from their house-door by that track
    The bride and bridegroom went ;
Sweet Mary, though she was not gay,
    Seem'd cheerful and content.

  * As they could be—1809.

But when they to the church-yard came,
    I've heard poor Mary say,
As soon as she stepp'd into the sun,
    Her heart it died away.

And when the Vicar join'd their hands,
    Her limbs did creep and freeze;
But when they pray'd,* she thought she saw
    Her mother on her knees.

And o'er the church-path they return'd—
    I saw poor Mary's back,
Just as she stepp'd beneath the boughs
    Into the mossy track.

Her feet upon the mossy track
    The married maiden set:
That moment—I have heard her say—
    She wish'd she could forget.

The shade o'er-flush'd her limbs with heat—
    Then came a chill like death:
And when the merry bells rang out,
    They seem'd to stop her breath.

Beneath the foulest mother's curse
    No child could ever thrive:
A mother is a mother still,
    The holiest thing alive.

* But when he pray'd—1809.

So five months pass'd : the mother still
    Would never heal the strife ;
But Edward was a loving man,
    And Mary a fond wife.

" My sister may not visit us,
    My mother says her nay :
O Edward ! you are all to me,
I wish for your sake I could be
    More lifesome and more gay.

" I'm dull and sad ! indeed, indeed
    I know I have no reason !
Perhaps I am not well in health,
    And 'tis a gloomy season."

'Twas a drizzly time—no ice, no snow !
    And on the few fine days
She stirr'd not out, lest she might meet
    Her mother in the ways.

But Ellen, spite of miry ways
    And weather dark* and dreary,
Trudged every day to Edward's house,
    And made them all more cheery.

Oh ! Ellen was a faithful friend,
    More dear than any sister !
As cheerful too as singing lark ;

    * Dank—1809.

And she ne'er left them till 'twas dark,
　And then they always miss'd her.

And now Ash-Wednesday came—that day
　But few to church repair :
For on that day you know we read
　The Commination prayer.

Our late old Vicar, a kind man,
　Once, sir, he said to me,
He wish'd that service was clean out
　Of our good liturgy.

The mother walk'd into the church—
　To Ellen's seat she went :
Though Ellen always kept her church
　All church-days during Lent.

And gentle Ellen welcomed her
　With courteous looks and mild :
Thought she, " What if her heart should melt,
　And all be reconciled !"

The day was scarcely like a day—
　The clouds were black outright :
And many a night, with half a moon,
　I've seen the church more light.

The wind was wild ; against the glass
　The rain did beat and bicker ;

The church-tower swinging * over head,
  Your scarce could hear the Vicar !

And then and there the mother knelt,
  And audibly she cried—
" Oh ! may a clinging curse consume
  This woman by my side !

" O hear me, hear me, Lord in Heaven,
  Although thou take my life—
O curse this woman, at whose house
  Young Edward woo'd his wife.

By night and day, in bed and bower,
  O let her cursed be !"
So having pray'd, steady and slow,
  She rose up from her knee,
And left the church, nor e'er again
  The church-door enter'd she.

I saw poor Ellen kneeling still,
  So pale, I guess'd not why :
When she stood up, there plainly was
  A trouble in her eye.

And when the prayers were done, we all
  Came round and ask'd her why :
Giddy she seem'd, and sure there was
  A trouble in her eye.

* Swaying—1809—1817.

But ere she from the church-door stepp'd
    She smiled and told us why :
" It was a wicked woman's curse,"
    Quoth she, " and what care I ?"

She smiled, and smiled, and pass'd it off
    Ere from the door she stept—
But all agree it would have been
    Much better had she wept.

And if her heart was not at ease,
    This was her constant cry—
" It was a wicked woman's curse—
    God's good, and what care I ?"

There was a hurry in her looks,
    Her struggles she redoubled :
" It was a wicked woman's curse,
    And why should I be troubled ?"

These tears will come—I dandled her
    When 'twas the merest fairy—
Good creature ! and she hid it all :
    She told it not to Mary.

But Mary heard the tale : her arms
    Round Ellen's neck she threw ;
" O Ellen, Ellen, she cursed me,
    And now she hath* cursed you !"

* Has—1809.

I saw young Edward by himself
　　Stalk fast adown the lee,
He snatch'd a stick from every fence,
　　A twig from every tree.

He snapp'd them still with hand or knee,
　　And then away they flew !
As if with his uneasy limbs
　　He knew not what to do !

You see, good sir ! that single hill ?
　　His farm lies underneath :
He heard it there, he heard it all,
　　And only gnash'd his teeth.

Now Ellen was a darling love
　　In all his joys and cares :
And Ellen's name and Mary's name
Fast-link'd they both together came,
　　Whene'er he said his prayers.

And in the moment of his prayers
　　He loved them both alike :
Yea, both sweet names with one sweet joy
　　Upon his heart did strike !

He reach'd his home, and by his looks
　　They saw his inward strife :
And they clung round him with their arms,
　　Both Ellen and his wife.

And Mary could not check her tears,
  So on his breast she bow'd;
Then frenzy melted into grief,
  And Edward wept aloud.

Dear Ellen did not weep at all,
  But closelier did she cling,
And turn'd her face and look'd as if
  She saw some frightful thing.


### PART IV.

TO see a man tread over graves
  I hold it no good mark;
'Tis wicked in the sun and moon,
  And bad luck in the dark!

You see that grave? The Lord he gives,
  The Lord he takes away:
O Sir! the child of my old age
  Lies there as cold as clay.

Except that grave, you scarce see one
  That was not dug by me;
I'd rather dance upon 'em all
  Than tread upon these three!

"Ay, Sexton! 'tis a touching tale."
  You, sir! are but a lad;

This month I'm in my seventieth year,
    And still it makes me sad.

And Mary's sister told it me,
    For three good hours and more;
Though I had heard it, in the main,
    From Edward's self before.

Well! it pass'd off! the gentle Ellen
    Did well nigh dote on Mary;
And she went oftener than before,
And Mary loved her more and more:
    She managed all the dairy.

To market she on market-days,
    To church on Sundays came;
All seem'd the same: all seem'd so, sir!
    But all was not the same!

Had Ellen lost her mirth? Oh! no!
    But she was seldom cheerful;
And Edward look'd as if he thought
    That Ellen's mirth was fearful.

When by herself, she to herself
    Must sing some merry rhyme;
She could not now be glad for hours,
    Yet silent all the time.

And when she soothed her friend, through all
    Her soothing words 'twas plain

She had a sore grief of her own,
　A haunting in her brain.

And oft she said, I'm not grown thin !
　And then her wrist she spann'd ;
And once when Mary was down-cast,
　She took her by the hand,
And gazed upon her, and at first
　She gently press'd her hand ;

Then harder, till her grasp at length
　Did gripe like a convulsion !
" Alas !" said she, " we ne'er can be
　Made happy by compulsion ! "

And once her both arms suddenly
　Round Mary's neck she flung,
And her heart panted, and she felt
　The words upon her tongue.

She felt them coming, but no power
　Had she the words to smother ;
And with a kind of shriek she cried,
　" Oh Christ ! you're like your mother ! "

So gentle Ellen now no more
　Could make this sad house cheery ;
And Mary's melancholy ways
　Drove Edward wild and weary.

Lingering he raised his latch at eve,
　Though tired in heart and limb :

He loved no other place, and yet
   Home was no home to him.

One evening he took up a book,
   And nothing in it read ;
Then flung it down, and groaning cried,
   " O ! Heaven ! that I were dead."

Mary look'd up into his face,
   And nothing to him said ;
She tried to smile, and on his arm
   Mournfully lean'd her head.

And he burst into tears, and fell
   Upon his knees in prayer :
" Her heart is broke ! O God ! my grief,
   It is too great to bear !"

'Twas such a foggy time as makes
   Old sextons, sir ! like me,
Rest on their spades to cough ; the spring
   Was late uncommonly.

And then the hot days, all at once,
   They came, we knew not how :
You look'd about for shade, when scarce
   A leaf was on a bough.

It happen'd then ('twas in the bower,
   A furlong up the wood :
Perhaps you know the place, and yet
   I scarce know how you should,—)

No path leads thither, 'tis not nigh
    To any pasture-plot;
But cluster'd near the chattering brook,
    Lone hollies mark'd the spot.*

Those hollies of themselves a shape
    As of an arbour took,
A close, round arbour; and it stands
    Not three strides from a brook.†

Within this arbour, which was still
    With scarlet berries hung,
Were these three friends, one Sunday morn,
    Just as the first bell rung.

'Tis sweet to hear a brook, 'tis sweet
    To hear the Sabbath-bell,
'Tis sweet to hear them both at once
    Deep in a woody dell.

His limbs along the moss, his head
    Upon a mossy heap,
With shut-up senses, Edward lay:
That brook e'en on a working day
    Might chatter one to sleep.

And he had pass'd a restless night,
    And was not well in health;

* Some hollies mark the spot.—1809.
† From the brook.—*Ib.*

The women sat down by his side,
    And talk'd as 'twere by stealth.

" The Sun peeps through the close thick leaves,
    See, dearest Ellen ! see !
'Tis *in* the leaves, a little sun,
    No bigger than your ee ;

" A tiny sun, and it has got
    A perfect glory too ;
Ten thousand threads and hairs of light,
Make up a glory gay and bright
    Round that small orb so blue."

And then they argued of those rays,
    What colour they might be ;
Says this, " They're mostly green ;" says that,
    " They're amber-like to me."

So they sat chatting, while bad thoughts
    Were troubling Edward's rest ;
But soon they heard his hard quick pants,
    And the thumping in his breast.

" A mother too !" these self-same words
    Did Edward mutter plain ;
His face was drawn back on itself,
    With horror and huge pain.

Both groan'd at once, for both knew well
    What thoughts were in his mind ;

When he waked up, and stared like one
　　That hath been just struck blind.

He sat upright; and ere the dream
　　Had had time to depart,
"O God, forgive me!" (he exclaim'd)
　　"I have torn out her heart."

Then Ellen shriek'd, and forthwith burst
　　Into ungentle laughter;
And Mary shiver'd, where she sat,
　　And never she smiled after.

*Carmen reliquum in futurum tempus relegatum.*
To-morrow! and To-morrow! and To-morrow!——

# THE NIGHT-SCENE.

### A DRAMATIC FRAGMENT.

SANDOVAL.　You loved the daughter of Don
　　Manrique?
　*Earl Henry.*　　　　　　　　　　　Loved?
　*Sandoval.*　Did you not say you woo'd her?
　*Earl Henry.*　　　　　　　　　　　Once I loved
Her whom I dared not woo!
　*Sandoval.*　　　　　　And woo'd, perchance,
One whom you loved not!
　*Earl Henry.*　　　　　　Oh! I were most base,
Not loving Oropeza.　True, I woo'd her,
Hoping to heal a deeper wound; but she

Met my advances with impassion'd pride,
That kindled love with love.   And when her sire,
Who in his dream of hope already grasp'd
The golden circlet in his hand, rejected
My suit with insult, and in memory
Of ancient feuds pour'd curses on my head,
Her blessings overtook and baffled them !
But thou art stern, and with unkindly countenance
Art inly reasoning whilst thou listen'st to me.
 *Sandoval.* Anxiously, Henry ! reasoning
  anxiously.
But Oropeza—
 *Earl Henry.* Blessings gather round her !
Within this wood there winds a secret passage,
Beneath the walls, which opens out at length
Into the gloomiest covert of the garden.—
The night ere my departure to the army,
She, nothing trembling, led me through that gloom,
And to that covert by a silent stream,
Which, with one star reflected near its marge,
Was the sole object visible around me.
No leaflet stirr'd ; the air was almost sultry ;
So deep, so dark, so close, the umbrage o'er us !
No leaflet stirr'd ;—yet pleasure hung upon
The gloom and stillness of the balmy night-air.
A little further on an arbour stood,
Fragrant with flowering trees—I well remember
What an uncertain glimmer in the darkness
Their snow-white blossoms made—thither she led
 me,
To that sweet bower !   Then Oropeza trembled—

I heard her heart beat—if 'twere not my own.
    *Sandoval.*   A rude and scaring note, my friend !
    *Earl Henry.*                         Oh ! no !
I have small memory of aught but pleasure.
The inquietudes of fear, like lesser streams
Still flowing, still were lost in those of love :
So love grew mightier from the fear, and Nature,
Fleeing from pain, shelter'd herself in joy.
The stars above our heads were dim and steady,
Like eyes suffused with rapture.—Life was in us :
We were all life, each atom of our frames
A living soul—I vow'd to die for her :
With the faint voice of one who, having spoken,
Relapses into blessedness, I vow'd it :
That solemn vow, a whisper scarcely heard,
A murmur breathed against a lady's ear.
Oh ! there is joy above the name of pleasure,
Deep self-possession, an intense repose.
    *Sandoval* [*with a sarcastic smile*].  No other than
        as eastern sages paint,
The God, who floats upon a lotos-leaf,
Dreams for a thousand ages ; then awaking,
Creates a world, and smiling at the bubble,
Relapses into bliss.
    *Earl Henry.*         Ah ! was that bliss
Fear'd as an alien, and too vast for man ?
For suddenly, impatient of its silence,
Did Oropeza, starting, grasp my forehead.
I caught her arms ; the veins were swelling on them.
Through the dark bower she sent a hollow voice ;—
" Oh ! what if all betray me ? what if thou ? "

I swore, and with an inward thought that seem'd
The purpose and the substance of my being,
I swore to her, that were she red with guilt,
I would exchange my unblench'd state with hers.—
Friend ! by that winding passage, to that bower
I now will go—all objects there will teach me
Unwavering love, and singleness of heart.
Go, Sandoval ! I am prepared to meet her—
Say nothing of me—I myself will seek her—
Nay, leave me, friend ! I cannot bear the torment
And keen inquiry of that scanning eye.—

> [*Earl Henry retires into the wood.*]

*Sandoval* [*alone*].    O Henry ! always strivest
    thou to be great
By thine own act—yet art thou never great
But by the inspiration of great passion.
The whirl-blast comes, the desert-sands rise up
And shape themselves : from earth to heaven they
    stand,
As though they were the pillars of a temple,
Built by Omnipotence in its own honour !
But the blast pauses, and their shaping spirit
Is fled : the mighty columns were but sand,
And lazy snakes trail o'er the level ruins !


## TO A LADY.

### WITH FALCONER'S " SHIPWRECK."

AH ! not by Cam or Isis, famous streams,
    In arched groves, the youthful poet's choice ;

Nor while half-listening, 'mid delicious dreams,
    To harp and song from lady's hand and voice ;

Nor yet while gazing in sublimer mood
    On cliff, or cataract, in Alpine dell ;
Nor in dim cave with bladdery sea-weed strew'd,
    Framing wild fancies to the ocean's swell ;

Our sea-bard sang this song ! which still he sings,
    And sings for thee, sweet friend ! Hark, Pity,
        hark !
Now mounts, now totters on the tempest's wings,
    Now groans, and shivers, the replunging bark !

" Cling to the shrouds !" In vain ! The breakers
        roar—
    Death shrieks !   With two alone of all his clan
Forlorn the poet paced the Grecian shore,
    No classic roamer, but a shipwreck'd man !

Say then, what Muse inspired these genial strains
    And lit his spirit to so bright a flame ?
The elevating thought of suffer'd pains,
    Which gentle hearts shall mourn ; but chief, the
        name

Of gratitude ! remembrances of friend,
    Or absent or no more ! shades of the Past,
Which Love makes substance !   Hence to thee I
        send,
    O dear as long as life and memory last !

I send with deep regards of heart and head,
    Sweet maid, for friendship form'd ! this work to
      thee :
And thou, the while thou canst not choose but shed
    A tear for Falconer, wilt remember me.


## THE VISIONARY HOPE.

SAD lot, to have no hope ! Though lowly kneeling
    He fain would frame a prayer within his breast,
Would fain entreat for some sweet breath of healing,
That his sick body might have ease and rest ;
He strove in vain ! the dull sighs from his chest
Against his will the stifling load revealing,
Though Nature forced ; though like some captive
      guest,
Some royal prisoner at his conqueror's feast,
An alien's restless mood but half concealing,
The sternness on his gentle brow confess'd,
Sickness within and miserable feeling :
Though obscure pangs made curses of his dreams,
And dreaded sleep, each night repell'd in vain,
Each night was scatter'd by its own loud screams :
Yet never could his heart command, though fain,
One deep full wish to be no more in pain.

    That Hope, which was his inward bliss and boast,
Which waned and died, yet ever near him stood,
Though changed in nature, wander where he
      would—
For Love's despair is but Hope's pining ghost !

For this one hope he makes his hourly moan,
He wishes and can wish for this alone !
Pierced, as with light from Heaven, before its gleams
(So the love-stricken visionary deems)
Disease would vanish, like a summer shower,
Whose dews fling sunshine from the noon-tide
   bower !
Or let it stay ! yet this one Hope should give
Such strength that he would bless his pains and live.

## THE HAPPY HUSBAND.

### A FRAGMENT.

OFT, oft methinks, the while with thee,
 I breathe, as from the heart, thy dear
And dedicated name, I hear
A promise and a mystery,
 A pledge of more than passing life,
 Yea, in that very name of Wife !

A pulse of love that ne'er can sleep !
 A feeling that upbraids the heart
 With happiness beyond desert,
That gladness half requests to weep !
 Nor bless I not the keener sense
 And unalarming turbulence

Of transient joys, that ask no sting
 From jealous fears, or coy denying ;
 But born beneath Love's brooding wing,

And into tenderness soon dying,
　　Wheel out their giddy moment, then
　　Resign the soul to love again ;—

A more precipitated vein
　　Of notes, that eddy in the flow
　　Of smoothest song, they come, they go,
And leave their sweeter understrain
　　Its own sweet self—a love of thee
　　That seems, yet cannot greater be !


## RECOLLECTIONS OF LOVE.

### I.

HOW warm this woodland wild Recess !
　　Love surely hath been breathing here ;
　　And this sweet bed of heath, my dear !
Swells up, then sinks with faint caress,
　　As if to have you yet more near.

### II.

Eight springs have flown, since last I lay
　　On sea-ward Quantock's heathy hills,
　　Where quiet sounds from hidden rills
Float here and there, like things astray,
　　And high o'er head the sky-lark shrills.

### III.

No voice as yet had made the air
　　Be music with your name ; yet why
　　That asking look ? that yearning sigh ?

That sense of promise every where?
   Beloved ! flew your spirit by?

### IV.

As when a mother doth explore
   The rose-mark on her long-lost child,
   I met, I loved you, maiden mild !
As whom I long had loved before—
   So deeply had I been beguiled.

### V.

You stood before me like a thought,
   A dream remember'd in a dream.
   But when those meek eyes first did seem
To tell me, Love within you wrought—
   O Greta, dear domestic stream !

### VI.

Has not, since then, Love's prompture deep,
   Has not Love's whisper evermore
   Been ceaseless, as thy gentle roar?
Sole voice, when other voices sleep,
   Dear undersong in Clamour's hour.

## AN ODE TO THE RAIN.

COMPOSED BEFORE DAYLIGHT, ON THE MORNING APPOINTED
   FOR THE DEPARTURE OF A VERY WORTHY, BUT NOT
   VERY PLEASANT VISITOR, WHOM IT WAS FEARED THE
   RAIN MIGHT DETAIN.

### I.

I KNOW it is dark ; and though I have lain,
   Awake, as I guess, an hour or twain,

I have not once open'd the lids of my eyes,
But I lie in the dark, as a blind man lies.
O Rain! that I lie listening to,
You're but a doleful sound at best:
I owe you little thanks, 'tis true,
For breaking thus my needful rest!
Yet if, as soon as it is light,
O Rain! you will but take your flight,
I'll neither rail, nor malice keep,
Though sick and sore for want of sleep.
But only now, for this one day,
Do go, dear Rain! do go away!

### II.

O Rain! with your dull two-fold sound,
The clash hard by, and the murmur all round!
You know, if you know aught, that we,
Both night and day, but ill agree:
For days and months, and almost years,
Have limp'd on through this vale of tears,
Since body of mine, and rainy weather,
Have lived on easy terms together.
Yet if, as soon as it is light,
O Rain! you will but take your flight,
Though you should come again to-morrow,
And bring with you both pain and sorrow;
Though stomach should sicken and knees should
    swell—
I'll nothing speak of you but well.
But only now for this one day,
Do go, dear Rain! do go away!

### III.

Dear Rain ! I ne'er refused to say
You're a good creature in your way ;
Nay, I could write a book myself,
Would fit a parson's lower shelf,
Showing how very good you are.—
What then ? sometimes it must be fair !
And if sometimes, why not to-day ?
Do go, dear Rain ! do go away !

### IV.

Dear Rain ! if I've been cold and shy,
Take no offence !   I'll tell you why.
A dear old Friend e'en now is here,
And with him came my sister dear ;
After long absence now first met,
Long months by pain and grief beset—
We three dear friends ! in truth, we groan
Impatiently to be alone.
We three, you mark ! and not one more !
The strong wish makes my spirit sore.
We have so much to talk about,
So many sad things to let out ;
So many tears in our eye-corners,
Sitting like little Jacky Horners—
In short, as soon as it is day,
Do go, dear Rain ! do go away.

### V.

And this I'll swear to you, dear Rain !
Whenever you shall come again,

Be you as dull as e'er you could
(And by the bye 'tis understood,
You're not so pleasant as you're good),
Yet, knowing well your worth and place,
I'll welcome you with cheerful face ;
And though you stay'd a week or more,
Were ten times duller than before ;
Yet with kind heart, and right good will,
I'll sit and listen to you still ;
Nor should you go away, dear Rain !
Uninvited to remain.
But only now, for this one day,
Do go, dear Rain ! do go away.


## ELEGY,

IMITATED FROM ONE OF AKENSIDE'S BLANK-VERSE
INSCRIPTIONS.

NEAR the lone pile with ivy overspread,
    Fast by the rivulet's sleep-persuading sound,
Where "sleeps the moonlight" on yon verdant
    bed—
    O humbly press that consecrated ground !

For there does Edmund rest, the learned swain !
    And there his spirit most delights to rove :
Young Edmund ! famed for each harmonious strain,
    And the sore wounds of ill-requited love.

Like some tall tree that spreads its branches wide,
　And loads the west-wind with its soft perfume,
His manhood blossom'd ; till the faithless pride
　Of fair Matilda sank him to the tomb.

But soon did righteous Heaven her guilt pursue !
　Where'er with wilder'd step she wander'd pale,
Still Edmund's image rose to blast her view,
　Still Edmund's voice accused her in each gale.

With keen regret, and conscious guilt's alarms,
　Amid the pomp of affluence she pined ;
Nor all that lured her faith from Edmund's arms
　Could lull the wakeful horror of her mind.

Go, Traveller ! tell the tale with sorrow fraught :
　Some tearful maid perchance, or blooming youth,
May hold it in remembrance ; and be taught
　That Riches cannot pay for Love or Truth.

## SEPARATION.

A SWORDED man whose trade is blood,
　　In grief, in anger, and in fear,
Thro' jungle, swamp, and torrent flood,
　I seek the wealth you hold so dear !

The dazzling charm of outward form,
　The power of gold, the pride of birth,
Have taken Woman's heart by storm—
　Usurp'd the place of inward worth.

Is not true Love of higher price
    Than outward form, though fair to see,
Wealth's glittering fairy-dome of ice,
    Or echo of proud ancestry?—

O! Asra, Asra! couldst thou see
    Into the bottom of my heart,
There's such a mine of Love for thee,
    As almost might supply desert!

(This separation is, alas!
    Too great a punishment to bear;
O! take my life, or let me pass
    That life, that happy life, with her!)

The perils, erst with steadfast eye
    Encounter'd, now I shrink to see—
Oh! I have heart enough to die—
    Not half enough to part from Thee!

## EPITAPH ON AN INFANT.

ITS balmy lips the infant blest
    Relaxing from its mother's breast,
How sweet it heaves the happy sigh
Of innocent satiety!

And such my infant's latest sigh!
O tell, rude stone! the passer by,
That here the pretty babe doth lie,
Death sang to sleep with Lullaby.

## TELL'S BIRTH-PLACE.

### IMITATED FROM STOLBERG.

#### I.

MARK this holy chapel well !
    The birthplace, this, of William Tell.
Here, where stands God's altar dread,
Stood his parents' marriage-bed.

#### II.

Here first, an infant to her breast,
Him his loving mother prest ;
And kiss'd the babe, and bless'd the day,
And pray'd as mothers use to pray.

#### III.

" Vouchsafe him health, O God ! and give
The child thy servant still to live !"
But God had destined to do more
Through him, than through an armed power.

#### IV.

God gave him reverence of laws,
Yet stirring blood in Freedom's cause—
A spirit to his rocks akin,
The eye of the hawk, and the fire therein !

#### V.

To Nature and to Holy Writ
Alone did God the boy commit :
Where flash'd and roar'd the torrent, oft
His soul found wings, and soar'd aloft !

VI.

The straining oar and chamois chase
Had form'd his limbs to strength and grace :
On wave and wind the boy would toss,
Was great, nor knew how great he was !

VII.

He knew not that his chosen hand,
Made strong by God, his native land
Would rescue from the shameful yoke
Of *Slavery*—the which he broke !


## HUMAN LIFE.

### ON THE DENIAL OF IMMORTALITY.

#### A FRAGMENT.

I F dead, we cease to be ; if total gloom
  Swallow up life's brief flash for aye, we fare
As summer-gusts, of sudden birth and doom,
  Whose sound and motion not alone declare,
But *are* their whole of being ! If the breath
Be Life itself, and not its task and tent,
If even a soul like Milton's can know death ;
  O Man ! thou vessel purposeless, unmeant,
Yet drone-hive strange of phantom purposes,
  Surplus of Nature's dread activity,
Which, as she gazed on some nigh-finish'd vase,
Retreating slow, with meditative pause,
  She form'd with restless hands unconsciously.
Blank accident ! nothing's anomaly !

If rootless thus, thus substanceless thy state,
Go, weigh thy dreams, and be thy hopes, thy fears,
The counter-weights!—Thy laughter and thy tears
Mean but themselves, each fittest to create
And to repay each other! Why rejoices
    Thy heart with hollow joy for hollow good?
    Why cowl thy face beneath the mourner's hood,
Why waste thy sighs, and thy lamenting voices,
    Image of image, ghost of ghostly elf,
That such a thing as thou feel'st warm or cold?
Yet what and whence thy gain, if thou withhold
    These costless shadows of thy shadowy self?
Be sad! be glad! be neither! seek, or shun!
Thou hast no reason why! Thou canst have none;
Thy being's being is contradiction.


## MOLES.

—THEY shrink in, as Moles
    (Nature's mute monks, live mandrakes
  of the ground)
Creep back from Light—then listen for its sound;—
See but to dread, and dread they know not why—
The natural alien of their negative eye.


## THE VISIT OF THE GODS.

### IMITATED FROM SCHILLER.

NEVER, believe me,
    Appear the Immortals,
Never alone:

Scarce had I welcomed the sorrow-beguiler,
Iacchus! but in came boy Cupid the smiler;
Lo! Phœbus the glorious descends from his
    throne!
They advance, they float in, the Olympians all!
    With divinities fills my
        Terrestrial hall!

      How shall I yield you
      Due entertainment,
       Celestial quire?
Me rather, bright guests! with your wings of up-
    buoyance
Bear aloft to your homes, to your banquets of joy-
    ance,
That the roofs of Olympus may echo my lyre!
Hah! we mount! on their pinions they waft up
    my soul!
      O give me the nectar!
      O fill me the bowl!

      Give him the nectar!
      Pour out for the poet,
       Hebe! pour free!
Quicken his eyes with celestial dew,
That Styx the detested no more he may view,
And like one of us Gods may conceit him to be!
Thanks, Hebe! I quaff it! Io Pæan, I cry!
      The wine of the Immortals
       Forbids me to die!

## THE PANG MORE SHARP THAN ALL.

### AN ALLEGORY.

#### I.

H E too has flitted from his secret nest,
    Hope's last and dearest child without a
        name !—
Has flitted from me, like the warmthless flame,
That makes false promise of a place of rest
To the tired Pilgrim's still believing mind ;—
Or like some Elfin Knight in kingly court,
Who having won all guerdons in his sport,
Glides out of view, and whither none can find !

#### II.

Yes ! he hath flitted from me—with what aim,
Or why, I know not ! 'Twas a home of bliss,
And he was innocent, as the pretty shame
Of babe, that tempts and shuns the menaced kiss,
From its twy-cluster'd hiding place of snow !
Pure as the babe, I ween, and all aglow
As the dear hopes, that swell the mother's breast—
Her eyes down gazing o'er her clasped charge ;—
Yet gay as that twice happy father's kiss,
That well might glance aside, yet never miss,
Where the sweet mark emboss'd so sweet a targe—
Twice wretched he who hath been doubly blest !

#### III.

Like a loose blossom on a gusty night
He flitted from me—and has left behind

(As if to them his faith he ne'er did plight)
Of either sex and answerable mind
Two playmates, twin-births of his foster-dame :—
The one a steady lad (Esteem he hight)
And Kindness is the gentler sister's name.
Dim likeness now, though fair she be and good,
Of that bright boy who hath us all forsook ;—
But in his full-eyed aspect when she stood,
And while her face reflected every look,
And in reflection kindled—she became
So like him, that almost she seem'd the same !

### IV.

Ah ! he is gone, and yet will not depart !—
Is with me still, yet I from him exiled !
For still there lives within my secret heart
The magic image of the magic Child,
Which there he made up-grow by his strong art,
As in that crystal* orb—wise Merlin's feat,—
The wondrous " World of Glass," wherein inisled
All long'd for things their beings did repeat ;—
And there he left it, like a Sylph beguiled,
To live and yearn and languish incomplete !

### V.

Can wit of man a heavier grief reveal ?
Can sharper pang from hate or scorn arise ?—
Yes ! one more sharp there is that deeper lies,
Which fond Esteem but mocks when he would
    heal.

* Faërie Queene, B. III. C. 2, S. 19.

Yet neither scorn nor hate did it devise,
But sad compassion and atoning zeal !
One pang more blighting-keen than hope betray'd !
And this it is my woeful hap to feel,
When, at her Brother's hest, the twin-born Maid
With face averted and unsteady eyes,
Her truant playmate's faded robe puts on ;
And inly shrinking from her own disguise
Enacts the faery Boy that's lost and gone.
O worse than all ! O pang all pangs above
Is Kindness counterfeiting absent Love !

## KUBLA KHAN : OR, A VISION IN A DREAM.

[OF THE FRAGMENT OF KUBLA KHAN.

THE following Fragment is here published at the request of a poet of great and deserved celebrity, and as far as the Author's own opinions are concerned, rather as a psychological curiosity than on the ground of any supposed *poetic* merits.

In the summer of the year 1797, the Author, then in ill health, had retired to a lonely farm-house between Porlock and Linton, on the Exmoor confines of Somerset and Devonshire. In consequence of a slight indisposition, an anodyne had been prescribed, from the effects of which he fell asleep in his chair at the moment that he was reading the following sentence, or words of the same substance, in " Purchas's Pilgrimage :" " Here the Khan Kubla commanded a palace to be built, and a stately garden thereunto. And thus ten miles of fertile ground were inclosed with a wall."* The Author continued for about three hours in a profound sleep, at least of the external senses, during which time he has the most vivid confidence, that he could not have composed less than from two to three hundred lines ; if that indeed can be called composition in which all the images rose up before him as things, with a parallel production of the correspondent expressions, without any sensation or consciousness of effort. On awaking he appeared to himself to have a distinct recollection of the whole, and taking his pen, ink, and paper, instantly and eagerly wrote down the lines that are here preserved. At this moment he was unfortunately called out by a person on business from Porlock, and detained by him above an hour, and on his return to his room, found, to his no small surprise and mortification, that though he still retained some vague and dim recollection of the general purport † of the vision, yet, with the exception of some eight or ten scattered lines and images, all the rest had passed away like the images on the surface of a stream into which a stone has been cast, but, alas ! without the after restoration of the latter.

Yet from the still surviving recollections in his mind,

---

* The exact words are these :—"In Xamdu did Cublai Can build a stately Palace, encompassing sixteene miles of plaine ground with a wall, wherein are fertile Meddowes, pleasant Springs, delightfull Streames, and all sorts of beasts of chase and game, and in the middest thereof a sumptuous house of pleasure."—PURCHAS *his Pilgrimage: Lond. fol.* 1626, Bk. 4. chap. 13, p. 418.—ED.

† Purpose—1816.

the Author has frequently purposed to finish for himself what had been originally, as it were, given to him. Αὔριον* ἄδιον ᾄσω : but the to-morrow is yet to come.

As a contrast to this vision, I have annexed a fragment of a very different character, describing with equal fidelity the dream of pain and disease.]

1816.

IN Xanadu did Kubla Khan
    A stately pleasure-dome decree :
Where Alph, the sacred river, ran
Through caverns measureless to man
    Down to a sunless sea.
So twice five miles of fertile ground
With walls and towers were girdled round :
And there were † gardens bright with sinuous rills
Where blossom'd many an incense-bearing tree ;
And here were forests ancient as the hills,
Enfolding ‡ sunny spots of greenery.

But oh ! that deep romantic chasm which slanted
Down the green hill athwart a cedarn cover !
A savage place ! as holy and enchanted
As e'er beneath a waning moon was haunted
By woman wailing for her demon-lover !
And from this chasm, with ceaseless turmoil seeth-
        ing,
As if this earth in fast thick pants were breathing,
A mighty fountain momently was forced :

* Σαμερον—1816.
† And here were, &c.—1816.        ‡ And folding—*ib.*

Amid whose swift half-intermitted burst
Huge fragments vaulted like rebounding hail,
Or chaffy grain beneath the thresher's flail :
And mid these dancing rocks at once and ever
It flung up momently the sacred river.
Five miles meandering with a mazy motion
Through wood and dale the sacred river ran,
Then reach'd the caverns measureless to man,
And sank in tumult to a lifeless ocean :
And 'mid this tumult Kubla heard from far
Ancestral voices prophesying war !

    The shadow of the dome of pleasure
    Floated midway on the waves ;
    Where was heard the mingled measure
    From the fountain and the caves.
It was a miracle of rare device,
A sunny pleasure-dome with caves of ice !

    A damsel with a dulcimer
    In a vision once I saw :
    It was an Abyssinian maid,
    And on her dulcimer she play'd,
    Singing of Mount Abora.
    Could I revive within me
    Her symphony and song,
    To such a deep delight 'twould win me
That with music loud and long,
I would build that dome in air,
That sunny dome ! those caves of ice !
And all who heard should see them there,

And all should cry, Beware ! Beware !
His flashing eyes, his floating hair !
Weave a circle round him thrice,
And close your eyes with holy dread,
For he on honey-dew hath fed,
And drunk* the milk of Paradise.


## THE PAINS OF SLEEP.

ERE on my bed my limbs I lay,
    It hath not been my use to pray
With moving lips or bended knees ;
But silently, by slow degrees,
My spirit I to Love compose,
In humble trust mine eye-lids close,
With reverential resignation,
No wish conceived, no thought exprest,
Only a sense of supplication ;
A sense o'er all my soul imprest
That I am weak, yet not unblest,
Since in me, round me, every where
Eternal Strength and Wisdom are.

But yester-night I pray'd aloud
In anguish and in agony,
Up-starting from the fiendish crowd
Of shapes and thoughts that tortured me :

* Drank—1816.

A lurid light, a trampling throng,
Sense of intolerable wrong,
And whom I scorn'd, those only strong !
Thirst of revenge, the powerless will
Still baffled, and yet burning still !
Desire with loathing strangely mix'd
On wild or hateful objects fix'd.
Fantastic passions ! maddening brawl !
And shame and terror over all !
Deeds to be hid which were not hid,
Which all confused I could not know
Whether I suffer'd, or I did :
For all seem'd guilt, remorse or woe,
My own or others still the same
Life-stifling fear, soul-stifling shame !

So two nights pass'd : the night's dismay
Sadden'd and stunn'd the coming day.
Sleep, the wide blessing, seem'd to me
Distemper's worst calamity.
The third night, when my own loud scream
Had waked me from the fiendish dream,
O'ercome with sufferings strange and wild,
I wept as I had been a child ;
And having thus by tears subdued
My anguish to a milder mood,
Such punishments, I said, were due
To natures deepliest stain'd with sin,—
For aye entempesting anew
The unfathomable hell within
The horror of their deeds to view,

To know and loathe, yet wish and do !
Such griefs with such men well agree,
But wherefore, wherefore fall on me ?
To be beloved is all I need,
And whom I love, I love indeed.

## LIMBO.

'TIS a strange place, this Limbo !—not a place,
    Yet name it so ;—where Time and weary Space
Fetter'd from flight, with night-mare sense of flee-
    ing,
Strive for their last crepuscular half-being ;—
Lank Space, and scytheless Time with branny hands
Barren and soundless as the measuring sands,
Not mark'd by flit of Shades,—unmeaning they
As moonlight on the dial of the day !
But that is lovely—looks like human Time,—
An old man with a steady look sublime,
That stops his earthly task to watch the skies ;
But he is blind— a statue hath such eyes ;—
Yet having moonward turn'd his face by chance,
Gazes the orb with moon-like countenance,
With scant white hairs, with foretop bald and high,
He gazes still,—his eyeless face all eye ;—
As 'twere an organ full of silent sight,
His whole face seemeth to rejoice in light !—
Lip touching lip, all moveless, bust and limb—
He seems to gaze at that which seems to gaze on him !
    No such sweet sights doth Limbo den immure,
Wall'd round, and made a spirit-jail secure,

By the mere horror of blank Nought-at-all,
Whose circumambience doth these ghosts enthral.
A lurid thought is growthless, dull Privation,
Yet that is but a Purgatory curse ;
Hell knows a fear far worse,
A fear—a future state ;—'tis positive Negation !


## NE PLUS ULTRA.

SOLE Positive of Night !
  Antipathist of Light !
Fate's only essence ! primal scorpion rod—
The one permitted opposite of God !—
Condensed blackness and abysmal storm
  Compacted to one sceptre
   Arms the Grasp enorm—
   The Intercepter—
The Substance that still casts the shadow Death !—
  The Dragon foul and fell—
   The unrevealable,
And hidden one, whose breath
Gives wind and fuel to the fires of Hell !—
  Ah ! sole despair
 Of both th' eternities in Heaven !
Sole interdict of all-bedewing prayer,
  The all-compassionate !
  Save to the Lampads Seven
Reveal'd to none of all th' Angelic State,
  Save to the Lampads Seven,
  That watch the throne of Heaven !

## FRAGMENT OF A POEM

ENTITLED, "THE WANDERINGS OF CAIN."

ENCINCTURED with a twine of leaves,
    That leafy twine his only dress!
A lovely boy was plucking fruits,
By moonlight, in a wilderness.
The moon was bright, the air was free,
And fruits and flowers together grew
On many a shrub and many a tree:
And all put on a gentle hue,
Hanging in the shadowy air
Like a picture rich and rare.
It was a climate where, they say,
The night is more beloved than day.
But who that beauteous boy beguiled,
That beauteous boy to linger here?
Alone, by night, a little child,
In place so silent and so wild—
Has he no friend, no loving mother near?


## ISRAEL'S LAMENT.*

MOURN, Israel! Sons of Israel, mourn!
    Give utterance to the inward throe!

* Translation of "A Hebrew Dirge, chanted in the Great
Synagogue, St. James's Place, Aldgate, on the day of the

As wails, of her first love forlorn,
   The Virgin clad in robes of woe.

Mourn the young Mother, snatch'd away
   From Light and Life's ascending Sun !
Mourn for the babe, Death's voiceless prey,
   Earn'd by long pangs and lost ere won.

Mourn the bright Rose that bloom'd and went
   Ere half disclosed its vernal hue !
Mourn the green bud, so rudely rent,
   It brake the stem on which it grew.

Mourn for the universal woe
   With solemn dirge and faltering tongue :
For England's Lady is laid low,
   So dear, so lovely, and so young !

The blossoms on her Tree of Life
   Shone with the dews of recent bliss :
Transplanted in that deadly strife,
   She plucks its fruits in Paradise.

Mourn for the widow'd Lord in chief,
   Who wails and will not solaced be !
Mourn for the childless Father's grief,
   The wedded Lover's agony !

Funeral of her Royal Highness the Princess Charlotte, by
Hyman Hurwitz, Master of the Hebrew Academy, Highgate, 1817." The Hebrew text with Coleridge's translation
appeared at the time in a separate pamphlet form.—Ed.

Mourn for the Prince, who rose at morn
    To seek and bless the firstling bud
Of his own Rose, and found the thorn,
    Its point bedew'd with tears of blood.

O press again that murmuring string !
    Again bewail that princely Sire !
A destined Queen, a future King,
    He mourns on one funereal pyre.

Mourn for Britannia's hopes decay'd,
    Her daughters wail their dear defence ;
Their fair example, prostrate laid,
    Chaste Love and fervid Innocence.

While Grief in song shall seek repose,
    We will take up a Mourning yearly :
To wail the blow that crush'd the Rose,
    So dearly prized and loved so dearly.

Long as the fount of Song o'erflows
    Will I the yearly dirge renew :
Mourn for the firstling of the Rose
    That snapt the stem on which it grew.

The proud shall pass, forgot ; the chill,
    Damp, trickling Vault their only mourner !
Not so the regal Rose, that still
    Clung to the breast which first had worn her !

———

O thou, who mark'st the Mourner's path
    To sad Jeshurun's Sons attend !
Amid the Lightnings of thy Wrath
    The showers of Consolation send !

Jehovah frowns ! the Islands bow !
    And Prince and People kiss the Rod !—
Their dread chastising Judge wert thou,
    Be thou their Comforter, O God !

1817.


## ALICE DU CLOS :

### OR THE FORKED TONGUE. A BALLAD.

"One word with two meanings is the traitor's shield and
shaft : and a slit tongue be his blazon !"

*Caucasian Proverb.*

"THE Sun is not yet risen,
    But the dawn lies red on the dew :
Lord Julian has stolen from the hunters away,
    Is seeking, Lady, for you.
Put on your dress of green,
    Your buskins and your quiver ;
Lord Julian is a hasty man,
    Long waiting brook'd he never.
I dare not doubt him, that he means
    To wed you on a day,
Your lord and master for to be,
    And you his lady gay.

O Lady ! throw your book aside !
I would not that my Lord should chide."

Thus spake Sir Hugh the vassal knight
　　To Alice, child of old Du Clos,
As spotless fair, as airy light
　　As that moon-shiny doe,
The gold star on its brow, her sire's ancestral crest !
For ere the lark had left his nest,
　　She in the garden bower below
Sate loosely wrapt in maiden white,
Her face half drooping from the sight,
　　A snow-drop on a tuft of snow !

O close your eyes, and strive to see
The studious maid, with book on knee,—
　　Ah ! earliest-open'd flower ;
While yet with keen unblunted light
The morning star shone opposite
　　The lattice of her bower—
Alone of all the starry host,
　　As if in prideful scorn
Of flight and fear he stay'd behind,
　　To brave th' advancing morn.

O ! Alice could read passing well,
　　And she was conning then
Dan Ovid's mazy tale of loves,
　　And gods, and beasts, and men.

The vassal's speech, his taunting vein,
It thrill'd like venom thro' her brain ;

Yet never from the book
She raised her head, nor did she deign
　　The knight a single look.

" Off, traitor friend ! how darest thou fix
　　Thy wanton gaze on me ?
And why, against my earnest suit,
　　Does Julian send by thee ?

" Go, tell thy Lord, that slow is sure :
　　Fair speed his shafts to-day !
I follow here a stronger lure,
　　And chase a gentler prey."

She said : and with a baleful smile
　　The vassal knight reel'd off—
Like a huge billow from a bark
　　Toil'd in the deep sea-trough,
That shouldering sideways in mid plunge,
　　Is traversed by a flash ;
And staggering onward, leaves the ear
　　With dull and distant crash.

And Alice sate with troubled mien
A moment ; for the scoff was keen,
　　And thro' her veins did shiver !
Then rose and donn'd her dress of green,
　　Her buskins and her quiver.

There stands the flowering may-thorn tree !
From thro' the veiling mist you see
　　The black and shadowy stem ;—

Smit by the sun the mist in glee
Dissolves to lightsome jewelry—
　　Each blossom hath its gem !


With tear-drop glittering to a smile,
The gay maid on the garden-stile
　　Mimics the hunter's shout.
" Hip ! Florian, hip ! To horse, to horse !
　　Go, bring the palfrey out.


" My Julian's out with all his clan,
　　And, bonny boy, you wis,
Lord Julian is a hasty man,
　　Who comes late, comes amiss."


Now Florian was a stripling squire,
　　A gallant boy of Spain,
That toss'd his head in joy and pride
Behind his Lady fair to ride,
　　But blush'd to hold her train.


The huntress is in her dress of green,—
And forth they go ; she with her bow,
　　Her buskins and her quiver !—
The squire—no younger e'er was seen—
With restless arm and laughing een,
　　He makes his javelin quiver.


And had not Ellen stay'd the race,
And stopp'd to see, a moment's space,
　　The whole great globe of light

Give the last parting kiss-like touch
To the eastern ridge, it lack'd not much,
   They had o'erta'en the knight.

It chanced that up the covert lane,
   Where Julian waiting stood,
A neighbour knight prick'd on to join
   The huntsmen in the wood.

And with him must Lord Julian go,
   Tho' with an anger'd mind :
Betroth'd not wedded to his bride,
In vain he sought, 'twixt shame and pride,
   Excuse to stay behind.

He bit his lip, he wrung his glove,
He look'd around, he look'd above,
   But pretext none could find or frame !
Alas ! alas ! and wel-a-day !
It grieves me sore to think, to say,
That names so seldom meet with Love,
   Yet Love wants courage without a name !

Straight from the forest's skirt the trees
   O'er-branching, made an aisle,
Where hermit old might pace and chaunt
   As in a minster's pile.

From underneath its leafy screen,
   And from the twilight shade,

You pass at once into a green,
    A green and lightsome glade.


And there Lord Julian sate on steed ;
    Behind him, in a round,
Stood knight and squire, and menial train ;
Against the leash the greyhounds strain ;
    The horses paw'd the ground.


When up the alley green, Sir Hugh
    Spurr'd in upon the sward,
And mute, without a word, did he
    Fall in behind his lord.


Lord Julian turn'd his steed half round.—
    " What ! doth not Alice deign
To accept your loving convoy, knight ?
Or doth she fear our woodland sleight,
    And joins us on the plain ? "


With stifled tones the knight replied,
And look'd askance on either side,—
    " Nay, let the hunt proceed !—
The Lady's message that I bear,
I guess would scantly please your ear,
    And less deserves your heed.


" You sent betimes.   Not yet unbarr'd
    I found the middle door ;—
Two stirrers only met my eyes,
    Fair Alice, and one more.

" I came unlook'd for : and, it seem'd,
   In an unwelcome hour ;
And found the daughter of Du Clos
   Within the latticed bower.

" But hush ! the rest may wait.   If lost,
   No great loss, I divine ;
And idle words will better suit
   A fair maid's lips than mine."

" God's wrath ! speak out, man," Julian cried,
   O'ermaster'd by the sudden smart ;—
And feigning wrath, sharp, blunt, and rude,
The knight his subtle shift pursued.—
" Scowl not at me ; command my skill,
To lure your hawk back, if you will,
   But not a woman's heart.

" ' Go !' (said she) ' tell him,—slow is sure ;
   Fair speed his shafts to-day !
I follow here a stronger lure,
   And chase a gentler prey.'

" The game, pardie, was full in sight,
That then did, if I saw aright,
   The fair dame's eyes engage ;
For turning, as I took my ways,
I saw them fix'd with steadfast gaze
   Full on her wanton page."

The last word of the traitor knight
   It had but enter'd Julian's ear,—

From two o'erarching oaks between,
With glistening helm-like cap is seen,
    Borne on in giddy cheer,

A youth, that ill his steed can guide ;
Yet with reverted face doth ride,
    As answering to a voice,
That seems at once to laugh and chide—
" Not mine, dear mistress," still he cried,
    " 'Tis this mad filly's choice."

With sudden bound, beyond the boy,
See ! see ! that face of hope and joy,
    That regal front ! those cheeks aglow !
Thou needed'st but the crescent sheen,
A quiver'd Dian to have been,
    Thou lovely child of old Du Clos !

Dark as a dream Lord Julian stood,
Swift as a dream, from forth the wood,
    Sprang on the plighted Maid !
With fatal aim, and frantic force,
The shaft was hurl'd !—a lifeless corse,
Fair Alice from her vaulting horse,
    Lies bleeding on the glade.


## THE KNIGHT'S TOMB.

WHERE is the grave of Sir Arthur O'Kellyn ?
        Where may the grave of that good man be ?—
By the side of a spring, on the breast of Helvellyn,

Under the twigs of a young birch tree !
The oak that in summer was sweet to hear,
And rustled its leaves in the fall of the year,
And whistled and roar'd in the winter alone,
Is gone,—and the birch in its stead is grown.—
The Knight's bones are dust,
And his good sword rust ;—
His soul is with the saints, I trust.*


## HYMN TO THE EARTH.

### HEXAMETERS.

EARTH ! thou mother of numberless children,
    the nurse and the mother,
Hail ! O Goddess, thrice hail ! Blest be thou ! and,
    blessing, I hymn thee !
Forth, ye sweet sounds ! from my harp, and my
    voice shall float on your surges—
Soar thou aloft, O my soul ! and bear up my song
    on thy pinions.

---

* The last three lines were quoted in the romance of *Ivanhoe*
(1820), vol. i. p. 156, while this fragment was still unpub-
lished, as follows : "To borrow lines from a contemporary
poet, who has written but too little :

    " The Knights are dust,
      And their good swords are rust,
    Their souls are with the saints, we trust."

From this circumstance Coleridge was convinced that Scott
was the author of the Waverley Novels. The lines were composed as an experiment for a metre, and repeated by the
author to a mutual friend, who repeated them again at a
dinner party to Scott, on the following day. (See Gillman's
*Life of Coleridge*, page 277.)

Travelling the vale with mine eyes—green meadows and lake with green island,
Dark in its basin of rock, and the bare stream
flowing in brightness,
Thrill'd with thy beauty and love in the wooded
slope of the mountain,
Here, great mother, I lie, thy child, with his head
on thy bosom !
Playful the spirits of noon, that rushing soft through
thy tresses,
Green-hair'd goddess ! refresh me ; and hark ! as
they hurry or linger,
Fill the pause of my harp, or sustain it with musical
murmurs.
Into my being thou murmurest joy, and tenderest
sadness
Shedd'st thou, like dew, on my heart, till the joy
and the heavenly sadness
Pour themselves forth from my heart in tears, and
the hymn of thanksgiving.

Earth ! thou mother of numberless children, the
nurse and the mother,
Sister thou of the stars, and beloved by the Sun,
the rejoicer !
Guardian and friend of the moon, O Earth, whom
the comets forget not,
Yea, in the measureless distance wheel round and
again they behold thee !
Fadeless and young (and what if the latest birth of
creation ?)

Bride and consort of Heaven, that looks down
        upon thee enamour'd !

Say, mysterious Earth ! O say, great mother and
        goddess,

Was it not well with thee then, when first thy lap
        was ungirdled,

Thy lap to the genial Heaven, the day that he
        woo'd thee and won thee !

Fair was thy blush, the fairest and first of the
        blushes of morning !

Deep was the shudder, O Earth ! the throe of thy
        self-retention :

Inly thou strovest to flee, and didst seek thyself at
        thy centre !

Mightier far was the joy of thy sudden resilience ;
        and forthwith

Myriad myriads of lives teem'd forth from the
        mighty embracement.

Thousand-fold tribes of dwellers, impell'd by thou-
        sand-fold instincts,

Fill'd, as a dream, the wide waters ; the rivers sang
        on their channels ;

Laugh'd on their shores the hoarse seas ; the yearn-
        ing ocean swell'd upward ;

Young life low'd through the meadows, the woods,
        and the echoing mountains,

Wander'd bleating in valleys, and warbled on blos-
        soming branches.

## WRITTEN DURING A TEMPORARY BLINDNESS,

### IN THE YEAR 1799.

O, WHAT a life is the eye ! what a strange and
　　inscrutable essence !
Him, that is utterly blind, nor glimpses the fire that
　　warms him ;
Him that never beheld the swelling breast of his
　　mother ;
Him that smiled in his gladness as a babe that
　　smiles in its slumber ;
Even for him it exists !  It moves and stirs in its
　　prison !
Lives with a separate life : and—" Is it a spirit ? "
　　he murmurs :
" Sure, it has thoughts of its own, and to see is
　　only a language ! "


## MAHOMET.

UTTER the song, O my soul ! the flight and re-
　　turn of Mohammed,
Prophet and priest, who scatter'd abroad both evil
　　and blessing,
Huge wasteful empires founded and hallow'd slow
　　persecution,
Soul-withering, but crush'd the blasphemous rites
　　of the Pagan
And idolatrous Christians.—For veiling the Gospel
　　of Jesus,

They, the best corrupting, had made it worse than
    the vilest.
Wherefore Heaven decreed th' enthusiast warrior
    of Mecca,
Choosing good from iniquity rather than evil from
    goodness.
    Loud the tumult in Mecca surrounding the fane
    of the idol ;—
Naked and prostrate the priesthood were laid—the
    people with mad shouts
Thundering now, and now with saddest ululation
Flew, as over the channel of rock-stone the ruinous
    river
Shatters its waters abreast, and in mazy uproar be-
    wilder'd,
Rushes dividuous all—all rushing impetuous on-
    ward.

## CATULLIAN HENDECASYLLABLES.*

HEAR, my beloved, an old Milesian story !—
    High, and embosom'd in congregated laurels,
Glimmer'd a temple upon a breezy headland ;
In the dim distance amid the skiey billows
Rose a fair island ; the god of flocks had placed it.
From the far shores of the bleak resounding island
Oft by the moonlight a little boat came floating,
Came to the sea-cave beneath the breezy headland,
Where amid myrtles a pathway stole in mazes
Up to the groves of the high embosom'd temple.
There in a thicket of dedicated roses,

* Freely translated from Mathisson's *Milesisches Mährchen.*

Oft did a priestess, as lovely as a vision,
Pouring her soul to the son of Cytherea,
Pray him to hover around the slight canoe-boat,
And with invisible pilotage to guide it
Over the dusk wave, until the nightly sailor
Shivering with ecstasy sank upon her bosom.

## DUTY SURVIVING SELF-LOVE,

### THE ONLY SURE FRIEND OF DECLINING LIFE.

#### A SOLILOQUY.

UNCHANGED within to see all changed without
　　Is a blank lot and hard to bear, no doubt.
Yet why at others' wanings should'st thou fret?
Then only might'st thou feel a just regret,
Hadst thou withheld thy love or hid thy light
In selfish forethought of neglect and slight.
O wiselier then, from feeble yearnings freed,
While, and on whom, thou may'st—shine on! nor
　　heed
Whether the object by reflected light
Return thy radiance or absorb it quite:
And though thou notest from thy safe recess
Old friends burn dim, like lamps in noisome air,
Love them for what they are; nor love them less,
Because to thee they are not what they were.

## PHANTOM OR FACT?

### A DIALOGUE IN VERSE.

#### AUTHOR.

A LOVELY form there sate beside my bed,
　　And such a feeding calm its presence shed,

A tender love so pure from earthly leaven,
That I unnethe * the fancy might control,
'Twas my own spirit newly come from heaven,
Wooing its gentle way into my soul !
But ah ! the change—It had not stirr'd, and yet—
Alas ! that change how fain would I forget !
That shrinking back, like one that had mistook !
That weary, wandering, disavowing look !
'Twas all another, feature, look, and frame,
And still, methought, I knew, it was the same !

FRIEND.

This riddling tale, to what does it belong ?
Is't history ? vision ? or an idle song ?
Or rather say at once, within what space
Of time this wild disastrous change took place ?

AUTHOR.

Call it a moment's work (and such it seems)
This tale's a fragment from the life of dreams ;
But say, that years matured the silent strife,
And 'tis a record from the dream of life.

PHANTOM.

ALL look and likeness caught from earth,
    All accident of kin and birth,
Had pass'd away.   There was no trace
Of aught on that illumined face,
Upraised beneath the rifted stone
But of one spirit all her own ;—
She, she herself, and only she,
Shone through her body visibly.

* *i. e.* scarcely, hardly.—ED.

## WORK WITHOUT HOPE.*

### LINES COMPOSED 21ST FEBRUARY,† 1827.

ALL Nature seems at work.   Slugs leave their
    lair--
The bees are stirring—birds are on the wing—
And Winter slumbering in the open air,
Wears on his smiling face a dream of Spring !
And I the while, the sole unbusy thing,
Nor honey make, nor pair, nor build, nor sing.

Yet well I ken the banks where amaranths blow,
Have traced the fount whence streams of nectar flow.
Bloom, O ye amaranths ! bloom for whom ye may,
For me ye bloom not !  Glide, rich streams, away !
With lips unbrighten'd, wreathless brow, I stroll :
And would you learn the spells that drowse my soul ?
Work without hope draws nectar in a sieve,
And Hope without an object cannot live.


## YOUTH AND AGE.‡

VERSE, a breeze mid blossoms straying,
    Where  Hope clung § feeding, like a bee—
Both were mine ! Life went a-maying
    With Nature, Hope, and Poesy,
        When I was young !

* Printed in *The Bijou*, Lond., William Pickering, 1828.
  † On a day in February—*Bijou.*
  ‡ Printed in *The Bijou*, 1828, and in *The Literary Souvenir*
of the same date.        § Clings—*Bijou.*

When I was young?—Ah, woful when!
Ah! for the change 'twixt Now and Then!
This breathing house* not built with hands,
This body that does me grievous wrong,
O'er aery cliffs and glittering sands,†
How lightly then it flash'd along :—
Like those trim skiffs,‡ unknown of yore,
On winding lakes and rivers wide,
That ask no aid of sail or oar,
That fear no spite of wind or tide!
Nought cared this body for wind or weather
When Youth and I lived in't together.§

Flowers are lovely; Love is flower-like;
Friendship is a sheltering tree;
O! the joys, that came down shower-like,
Of Friendship, Love, and Liberty,‖
                              Ere I was old!
Ere I was old? Ah woful Ere,**
Which tells me, Youth's no longer here!
O Youth! for years so many and sweet,††
'Tis known, that Thou and I were one,
I'll think it but a fond conceit—‡‡

---

* This house of clay—*Bijou.*
† O'er hill and dale and sounding sands—*ib.*
‡ Boats—*ib.*
§ See *Ode to the Rain, suprà,* p. 263.
‖ Of Beauty, Truth, and Liberty—1828.
** Ah mournful Ere—*Literary Souvenir.*
†† So merry and sweet—*Bijou.*
‡‡ False conceit—*ib.*

It cannot be that Thou art gone !
Thy vesper-bell hath not yet toll'd :—
And thou wert aye a masker bold !
What strange disguise hast now put on,
To make believe, that Thou art gone ?
I see these locks in silvery slips,
This drooping gait,* this alter'd size :
But spring-tide blossoms on thy lips,
And tears take sunshine from thine eyes !
Life is but thought : so think I will
That Youth and I are house-mates still.†

Dew-drops are the gems of morning,
But the tears of mournful eve !
Where no hope is, life's a warning
That only serves to make us grieve,
　　　　　　　　When we are old : ‡
That only serves to make us grieve
With oft and tedious taking-leave,
Like some poor nigh-related guest,

---

\* This dragging gait—*Bijou.*

† Here the poem ends in *The Bijou,* and the *Literary Souvenir.* The remaining portion was published under the title
of " The Old Man's Sigh, a Sonnet," dated " The Grove,
Highgate, 18th May, 1832," in *Blackwood's Magazine,* June
1832.

‡ That only serves to make us grieve
　　In our old age,
　Whose bruised wings quarrel with the bars of the still
　　narrowing cage.—1832.

That may not rudely be dismist ;
Yet hath outstay'd his welcome while,
And tells the jest without the smile.
[O ! might Life cease ! and Selfless Mind,
Whose total Being is Act, alone remain behind ! ]

## A DAY-DREAM.*

MY eyes make pictures, when they are shut :
    I see a fountain, large and fair,
A willow and a ruin'd hut,
    And thee, and me and Mary there.
O Mary ! make thy gentle lap our pillow !
Bend o'er us, like a bower, my beautiful green
      willow !

A wild-rose roofs the ruin'd shed,
    And that and summer well † agree :
And lo ! where Mary leans her head,
    Two dear names carved upon the tree !
And Mary's tears, they are not tears of sorrow :
Our sister and our friend will both be here to-morrow.

'Twas day : but now few, large, and bright,
    The stars are round the crescent moon ;
And now it is a dark warm night,
    The balmiest of the month of June !

* Printed in *The Bijou*, 1828.
† In *The Bijou* " will agree,"—probably a misprint.

A glow-worm fall'n, and * on the marge remounting
Shines, and its shadow shines, fit stars for our sweet
    fountain.

O ever—ever be thou blest !
    For dearly, Asra, love I thee ! †
This brooding warmth across my breast,
    This depth of tranquil bliss—ah, me !
Fount, tree and shed are gone, I know not whither,
But in one quiet room we three are still together.

The shadows dance upon the wall,
    By the still dancing fire-flames made ;
And now they slumber moveless all !
    And now they melt to one ‡ deep shade !
But not from me shall this mild darkness steal thee :
I dream thee with mine eyes, and at my heart I feel
    thee !

Thine eyelash on my cheek doth play—
    'Tis Mary's hand upon my brow !
But let me check this tender lay
    Which none may hear but she and thou !
Like the still hive at quiet midnight humming,
Murmur it to yourselves, ye two beloved women !

## FIRST ADVENT OF LOVE.

O FAIR is Love's first hope to gentle mind !
    As Eve's first star thro' fleecy cloudlet peeping ;

---

\* In the marge—*Bijou*.  † O Asra ! dearly love I thee !—*ib.*
‡ They make to me—*ib.*

And sweeter than the gentle south-west wind,
O'er willowy meads and shadow'd waters creeping,
And Ceres' golden fields ;—the sultry hind
Meets it with brow uplift, and stays his reaping.

## NAMES.*

I ASK'D my fair one happy day,
   What I should call her in my lay ;
  By what sweet name from Rome or Greece ;
Lalage, Neæra, Chloris,
Sappho, Lesbia, or Doris,
  Arethusa or Lucrece.

" Ah !" replied my gentle fair,
" Beloved, what are names but air ?
  Choose thou whatever suits the line ;
Call me Sappho, call me Chloris,
Call me Lalage or Doris,
  Only, only call me thine."

## WATER BALLAD.†

"COME hither, gently rowing,
   Come bear me quickly o'er
This stream so brightly flowing
  To yonder woodland shore.

* *Morning Post*, August 27, 1799 ; and, with the names given somewhat differently, in *The Keepsake* for 1829.

† *The Athenæum*, Oct. 29, 1831. [Now first included in any collection of Coleridge's Poems.]

But vain were my endeavour
    To pay thee, courteous guide ;
Row on, row on, for ever
    I'd have thee by my side.


" Good boatman, prithee haste thee,
I seek my father-land."—
' Say, when I there have placed thee,
    Dare I demand thy hand?'
" A maiden's head can never
    So hard a point decide ;
Row on, row on, for ever
    I'd have thee by my side."


The happy bridal over
    The wanderer ceased to roam,
For, seated by her lover,
    The boat became her home.
And still they sang together
    As steering o'er the tide :
" Row on through wind and weather
    For ever by my side."


## DESIRE.

WHERE true Love burns Desire is Love's pure
        flame ;
It is the reflex of our earthly frame,
That takes its meaning from the nobler part,
And but translates the language of the heart.

## LOVE AND FRIENDSHIP OPPOSITE.

HER attachment may differ from yours in degree,
  Provided they are both of one kind ;
But Friendship how tender so ever it be
  Gives no accord to Love, however refined.

Love, that meets not with Love, its true nature
      revealing,
  Grows ashamed of itself, and demurs :
If you cannot lift hers up to your state of feeling,
  You must lower down your state to hers.


## NOT AT HOME.

THAT Jealousy may rule a mind
    Where Love could never be
I know; but ne'er expect to find
    Love without Jealousy.

She has a strange cast in her ee,
    A swart sour-visaged maid—
But yet Love's own twin-sister she
    His house-mate and his shade.

Ask for her and she'll be denied :—
    What then ? they only mean
Their mistress has lain down to sleep,
    And can't just then be seen.

## TO A LADY,

OFFENDED BY A SPORTIVE OBSERVATION THAT
WOMEN HAVE NO SOULS.

NAY, dearest Anna! why so grave?
   I said, you had no soul, 'tis true!
For what you are, you cannot have:
   'Tis I that have one since I first had you!

———

I HAVE heard of reasons manifold
   Why Love must needs be blind,
But this the best of all I hold—
   His eyes are in his mind.

What outward form and feature are
   He guesseth but in part;
But what within is good and fair
   He seeth with the heart.


## LINES

SUGGESTED BY THE LAST WORDS OF BERENGARIUS.
OB. ANNO DOM. 1088.*

NO more 'twixt conscience staggering and the
   Pope
Soon shall I now before my God appear,

* *Literary Souvenir*, 1827.

By him to be acquitted, as I hope ;
By him to be condemned, as I fear.—


### REFLECTION ON THE ABOVE.

Lynx amid moles ! had I stood by thy bed,
Be of good cheer, meek soul ! I would have said :
I see a hope spring from that humble fear.
All are not strong alike through storms to steer
Right onward.   What though dread of threaten'd
      death
And dungeon torture made thy hand and breath
Inconstant to the truth within thy heart ?
That truth, from which, through fear, thou twice
      didst start,
Fear haply told thee, was a learned strife,
Or not so vital as to claim thy life :
And myriads had reach'd Heaven, who never knew
Where lay the difference 'twixt the false and true !

Ye, who secure 'mid trophies not your own,
Judge him who won them when he stood alone,
And proudly talk of recreant Berengare—
O first the age, and then the man compare !
That age how dark ! congenial minds how rare !
No host of friends with kindred zeal did burn !
No throbbing hearts awaited his return !

Prostrate alike when prince and peasant fell,
He only disenchanted from the spell,

Like the weak worm that gems the starless night,
Moved in the scanty circlet of his light :
And was it strange if he withdrew the ray
That did but guide the night-birds to their prey ?

The ascending day-star with a bolder eye
Hath lit each dew-drop on our trimmer lawn !
Yet not for this, if wise, shall we decry
The spots and struggles of the timid dawn ;
Lest so we tempt th' approaching noon to scorn
The mists and painted vapours of our morn.


## SANCTI DOMINICI PALLIUM;

### A DIALOGUE BETWEEN POET AND FRIEND,

FOUND WRITTEN ON THE BLANK LEAF AT THE BEGINNING
OF BUTLER'S BOOK OF THE CHURCH.

#### POET.

I NOTE the moods and feelings men betray,
　　And heed them more than aught they do or say ;
The lingering ghosts of many a secret deed
Still-born or haply strangled in its birth ;
These best reveal the smooth man's inward creed !
These mark the spot where lies the treasure Worth !

—— made up of impudence and trick,
With cloven tongue prepared to hiss and lick,
Rome's brazen serpent—boldly dares discuss
The roasting of thy heart, O brave John Huss !
And with grim triumph and a truculent glee

Absolves anew the Pope-wrought perfidy,
That made an empire's plighted faith a lie,
And fix'd a broad stare on the Devil's eye—
(Pleased with the guilt, yet envy-stung at heart
To stand outmaster'd in his own black art!)
Yet ——

FRIEND.

Enough of —— ! we're agreed,
Who now defends would then have done the deed.
But who not feels persuasion's gentle sway,
Who but must meet the proffer'd hand half way
When courteous ——

POET *(aside).*

(Rome's smooth go-between!)

FRIEND.

Laments the advice that sour'd a milky queen—
(For " bloody " all enlighten'd men confess
An antiquated error of the press :)
Who rapt by zeal beyond her sex's bounds,
With actual cautery staunch'd the Church's wounds !
And tho' he deems, that with too broad a blur
We damn the French and Irish massacre,
Yet blames them both—and thinks the Pope might
      err !
What think you now ?   Boots it with spear and
      shield
Against such gentle foes to take the field
Whose beckoning hands the mild Caduceus wield ?

POET.

What think I now? Even what I thought before;—
What —— boasts though —— may deplore,
Still I repeat, words lead me not astray
When the shown feeling points a different way.
Smooth —— can say grace at slander's feast,
And bless each haut-gout cook'd by monk or priest;
Leaves the full lie on ——'s gong to swell,
Content with half-truths that do just as well;
But duly decks his mitred comrade's flanks,
And with him shares the Irish nation's thanks!

So much for you, my friend! who own a Church,
And would not leave your mother in the lurch!
But when a Liberal asks me what I think—
Scared by the blood and soot of Cobbett's ink,
And Jeffrey's glairy phlegm and Connor's foam,
In search of some safe parable I roam—
An emblem sometimes may comprise a tome!

Disclaimant of his uncaught grandsire's mood,
I see a tiger lapping kitten's food:
And who shall blame him that he purs applause,
When brother Brindle pleads the good old cause;
And frisks his pretty tail, and half unsheathes his
        claws!
Yet not the less, for modern lights unapt,
I trust the bolts and cross-bars of the laws
More than the Protestant milk all newly lapt,
Impearling a tame wild-cat's whisker'd jaws!

## LINES

##### TO A COMIC AUTHOR, ON AN ABUSIVE REVIEW.

WHAT though the chilly wide-mouth'd quacking
   chorus
From the rank swamps of murk Review-land croak :
So was it, neighbour, in the times before us,
When Momus, throwing on his Attic cloak,
Romp'd with the Graces; and each tickled Muse
(That Turk, Dan Phœbus, whom bards call divine,
Was married to—at least, he kept—all nine)
Fled, but still with reverted faces ran ;
Yet, somewhat the broad freedoms to excuse,
They had allured the audacious Greek to use,
Swore they mistook him for their own good man.
This Momus—Aristophanes on earth
Men call'd him—maugre all his wit and worth,
Was croak'd and gabbled at. How, then, should you,
Or I, friend, hope to 'scape the skulking crew ?
No ! laugh, and say aloud, in tones of glee,
" I hate the quacking tribe, and they hate me ! "

## CONSTANCY TO AN IDEAL OBJECT.

SINCE all that beat about in Nature's range,
 Or veer or vanish ; why shouldst thou remain
The only constant in a world of change,
O yearning thought ! that livest but in the brain ?
Call to the hours, that in the distance play,

The faery people of the future day—
Fond thought! not one of all that shining swarm
Will breathe on thee with life-enkindling breath,
Till when, like strangers sheltering from a storm,
Hope and Despair meet in the porch of Death!
Yet still thou haunt'st me; and though well I see,
She is not thou, and only thou art she,
Still, still as though some dear embodied good,
Some living love before my eyes there stood
With answering look a ready ear to lend,
I mourn to thee and say—" Ah! loveliest friend!
That this the meed of all my toils might be,
To have a home, an English home, and thee!"
Vain repetition! Home and thou are one.
The peacefull'st cot the moon shall shine upon,
Lull'd by the thrush and waken'd by the lark,
Without thee were but a becalmed bark,
Whose helmsman on an ocean waste and wide
Sits mute and pale his mouldering helm beside.
And art thou nothing? Such thou art, as when
The woodman winding westward up the glen
At wintry dawn, where o'er the sheep-track's maze
The viewless snow-mist weaves a glistening haze,
Sees full before him, gliding without tread,
An image* with a glory round its head;
The enamour'd rustic worships its fair hues,
Nor knows he makes the shadow he pursues!

---

* This phenomenon, which the author has himself experienced, and of which the reader may find a description in one
of the earlier volumes of the Manchester Philosophical Trans-

## MODERN CRITICS.*

NO private grudge they need, no personal spite :
  The *viva sectio* is its own delight !
All enmity, all envy, they disclaim,
Disinterested thieves of our good name :
Cool, sober murderers of their neighbours' fame !

———

THE poet in his lone yet genial hour
  Gives to his eye a magnifying power :
Or rather he emancipates his eyes
From the black shapeless accidents of size—
In unctuous cones of kindling coal,
Or smoke upwreathing from the pipe's trim bole,
    His gifted ken can see
    Phantoms of sublimity. †

actions, is applied figuratively in the following passage of the
*Aids to Reflection* (p. 220) :—

  "Pindar's fine remark respecting the different effects of
music, on different characters, holds equally true of Genius ;
as many as are not delighted by it are disturbed, perplexed,
irritated. The beholder either recognises it as a projected
form of his own being, that moves before him with a glory
round its head, or recoils from it as a spectre."

  * *Biographia Literaria* (Lond. 1817.), vol. ii. p. 118.

  † *Historie and Gests of Maxilian*, Blackwood's Magazine,
January, 1822.

## INSCRIPTION FOR A TIME-PIECE.*

NOW! it is gone.—Our brief hours travel post,
  Each with its thought or deed, its Why or
    How :—
But know, each parting hour gives up a ghost
To dwell within thee—an eternal now !
  1830.

## FANCY IN NUBIBUS :

### OR THE POET IN THE CLOUDS.

*A Sonnet composed on the Sea-Coast.**

O ! IT is pleasant, with a heart at ease,
    Just after sunset, or by moonlight skies,
To make the shifting clouds be what you please,
  Or let the easily persuaded eyes
Own each quaint likeness issuing from the mould
  Of a friend's fancy ; or with head bent low
And cheek aslant see rivers flow of gold
  'Twixt crimson banks ; and then, a traveller, go
From mount to mount through Cloudland, gorgeous
    land !
  Or listening to the tide, with closed sight,
Be that blind bard, who on the Chian strand
  By those deep sounds possess'd with inward light,
Beheld the Iliad and the Odyssee
Rise to the swelling of the voiceful sea.

* Printed at the end of *Specimens of the Table-talk of S.T.C.*
Lond. 1835, ii. 360.

† *Blackwood's Magazine*, November, 1819.

# THE BLOSSOMING OF THE SOLITARY DATE-TREE.

### A LAMENT.

[I SEEM to have an indistinct recollection of having read either in one of the ponderous tomes of George of Venice, or in some other compilation from the uninspired Hebrew writers, an apologue or Rabbinical tradition to the following purpose :

While our first parents stood before their offended Maker, and the last words of the sentence were yet sounding in Adam's ear, the guileful false serpent, a counterfeit and a usurper from the beginning, presumptuously took on himself the character of advocate or mediator, and pretending to intercede for Adam, exclaimed : " Nay, Lord, in thy justice, not so ! for the man was the least in fault. Rather let the Woman return at once to the dust, and let Adam remain in this thy Paradise." And the word of the Most High answered Satan : " The tender mercies of the wicked are cruel. Treacherous Fiend ! if with guilt like thine, it had been possible for thee to have the heart of a Man, and to feel the yearning of a human soul for its counterpart, the sentence, which thou now counsellest, should have been inflicted on thyself."

The title of the following poem was suggested by a fact mentioned by Linnæus, of a date-tree in a nobleman's garden which year after year had put forth a full show of blossoms, but never produced fruit, till a branch from another date-tree had been conveyed from a distance of some hundred leagues. The first leaf of the MS. from which the poem has been transcribed, and which contained the two or three introductory stanzas, is wanting : and the author has in vain taxed his memory to repair the loss. But a rude draught of the poem contains the substance of the stanzas, and the reader is requested to receive it as the substitute. It is not impossible, that some congenial spirit, whose years do not exceed those of the Author at the time the poem was written, may find a pleasure in restoring the Lament to its original integrity by a reduction of the thoughts to the requisite metre.]

### I.

BENEATH the blaze of a tropical sun the mountain peaks are the thrones of frost, through the absence of objects to reflect the rays. " What no one with us shares, seems scarce our own." The presence of a one,

The best beloved, who loveth me the best,

is for the heart, what the supporting air from within is for the hollow globe with its suspended car. Deprive it of this, and all without, that would have buoyed it aloft even to the seat of the gods, becomes a burthen and crushes it into flatness.

### II.

The finer the sense for the beautiful and the lovely, and the fairer and lovelier the object presented to the sense ; the more exquisite the individual's capacity of joy, and the more ample his means and opportunities of enjoyment, the more heavily will he feel the ache of solitariness, the more unsubstantial becomes the feast spread around him. What matters it whether in fact the viands and the ministering graces are shadowy or real, to him who has not hand to grasp nor arms to embrace them?

### III.

Imagination; honourable aims;
Free commune with the choir that cannot die;
Science and song; delight in little things,
The buoyant child surviving in the man;
Fields, forests, ancient mountains, ocean, sky,
With all their voices—O dare I accuse
My earthly lot as guilty of my spleen,
Or call my destiny niggard! O no! no!
It is her largeness, and her overflow,
Which being incomplete, disquieteth me so!

### IV.

For never touch of gladness stirs my heart,
But timorously beginning to rejoice
Like a blind Arab, that from sleep doth start
In lonesome tent, I listen for thy voice.
Beloved! 'tis not thine; thou art not there!
Then melts the bubble into idle air,
And wishing without hope I restlessly despair.

### V.

The mother with anticipated glee
Smiles o'er the child, that, standing by her chair

And flattening its round cheek upon her knee,
Looks up, and doth its rosy lips prepare
To mock the coming sounds.   At that sweet sight
She hears her own voice with a new delight;
And if the babe perchance should lisp the notes
      aright,

### VI.

Then is she tenfold gladder than before!
But should disease or chance the darling take,
What then avail those songs, which sweet of yore
Were only sweet for their sweet echo's sake?
Dear maid! no prattler at a mother's knee
Was e'er so dearly prized as I prize thee:
Why was I made for Love and Love denied to me?

## THE EXCHANGE.*

WE pledged our hearts, my love and I,—
      I in my arms the maiden clasping;
I could not tell the reason why,
      But, oh! I trembled like an aspen.

Her father's love she bade me gain;
      I went, and shook like any reed!
I strove to act the man—in vain!
      We had exchanged our hearts indeed.

* *Literary Souvenir,* 1826.

## LOVE'S BURIAL-PLACE.*

*Lady.* If Love be dead—*Poet.* And I aver it !
*Lady.* Tell me, Bard ! where Love lies buried ?

*Poet.* Love lies buried where 'twas born :
Oh, gentle dame ! think it no scorn
If, in my fancy, I presume
To call thy bosom poor Love's Tomb.
And on that tomb to read the line :—
" Here lies a Love that once seem'd mine,
But took a chill, as I divine,
And died at length of a decline."

## THE SUICIDE'S ARGUMENT.

E RE the birth of my life, if I wish'd it or no,
No question was ask'd me—it could not be so !
If the life was the question, a thing sent to try,
And to live on be Yes ; what can No be ? to die.

### NATURE'S ANSWER.

Is't return'd, as 'twas sent ? Is't no worse for the
wear ?
Think first, what you are ! Call to mind what you
were !
I gave you innocence, I gave you hope,
Gave health, and genius, and an ample scope.

* *The Amulet,* 1833.

Return you me guilt, lethargy, despair?
Make out the inventory; inspect, compare!
Then die—if die you dare!


## THE TWO FOUNTS.*

STANZAS ADDRESSED TO A LADY ON HER RECOVERY
WITH UNBLEMISHED LOOKS, FROM A SEVERE
ATTACK OF PAIN.

'TWAS my last waking thought, how it could be †
   That thou, sweet friend, such anguish shouldst
     endure;
When straight from Dreamland came a Dwarf,
   and he
Could tell the cause, forsooth, and knew the cure.

Methought he fronted me with peering look
Fix'd on my heart; and read aloud in game
The loves and griefs therein, as from a book;
And utter'd praise like one who wish'd to blame.

In every heart (quoth he) since Adam's sin
Two Founts there are, of suffering and of cheer!
That to let forth, and this to keep within!
But she, whose aspect I find imaged here,

Of Pleasure only will to all dispense,
That Fount alone unlock, by no distress

* *Annual Register*, 1827; *Bijou*, 1828.
† How can it be—*A. R.*

Choked or turn'd inward, but still issue thence
Unconquer'd cheer, persistent loveliness.

As on the driving cloud the shiny bow,
That gracious thing made up of tears and light,
Mid the wild rack and rain that slants below
Stands smiling forth, unmoved and freshly bright ;—

As though the spirits of all lovely flowers,
Inweaving each its wreath and dewy crown,
Or ere they sank to earth in vernal showers,
Had built a bridge to tempt the angels down.

Even so, Eliza ! on that face of thine,
On that benignant face, whose look alone
(The soul's translucence thro' her crystal shrine !)
Has power to soothe all anguish but thine own,

A beauty hovers still, and ne'er takes wing,
But with a silent charm compels the stern
And torturing* Genius of the bitter spring,
To shrink aback, and cower upon his urn.

Who then needs wonder, if (no outlet found
In passion, spleen, or strife,) the fount of pain
O'erflowing beats against its lovely mound,
And in wild flashes shoots from heart to brain ?

Sleep, and the Dwarf with that unsteady gleam
On his raised lip, that aped a critic smile,
Had pass'd : yet I, my sad thoughts to beguile,
Lay weaving on the tissue of my dream ;

* Fostering—1827-28 (probably a misprint).—Ed.

Till audibly at length I cried, as though
Thou hadst indeed been present to my eyes,
O sweet, sweet sufferer ; if the case be so,
I pray thee, be less good, less sweet, less wise !

In every look a barbed arrow send,
On those soft lips let scorn and anger live !
Do any thing, rather than thus, sweet friend !
Hoard for thyself the pain thou wilt not give !

---

\* Yes, yes ! that boon, life's richest treat,
He had, or fancied that he had ;
Say, 'twas but in his own conceit—
    The fancy made him glad !
Crown of his cup, and garnish of his dish,
The boon, prefigured in his earliest wish,
The fair fulfilment of his poesy,
When his young heart first yearn'd for sympathy !

But e'en the meteor offspring of the brain
        Unnourish'd wane ;
Faith asks her daily bread,
And Fancy must be fed.
Now so it chanced—from wet or dry,
It boots not how—I know not why—
She miss'd her wonted food ; and quickly
Poor Fancy stagger'd and grew sickly.

* Printed in *The Amulet*, 1828, at the end of a Dialogue in Prose.

Then came a restless state, 'twixt yea and nay,
His faith was fix'd, his heart all ebb and flow ;
Or like a bark, in some half-shelter'd bay,
Above its anchor driving to and fro.

That boon, which but to have possest
In a belief, gave life a zest—
Uncertain both what it had been,
And if by error lost, or luck ;
And what it was ;—an evergreen
Which some insidious blight had struck,
Or annual flower, which, past its blow,
No vernal spell shall e'er revive ;
Uncertain, and afraid to know,
    Doubts toss'd him to and fro ;
Hope keeping Love, Love Hope alive,
Like babes bewilder'd in the snow,
That cling and huddle from the cold
In hollow tree or ruin'd fold.

Those sparkling colours, once his boast,
    Fading one by one away,
Thin and hueless as a ghost,
    Poor Fancy on her sick-bed lay ;
Ill at distance, worse when near,
Telling her dreams to jealous Fear !
Where was it then, the sociable sprite
That crown'd the Poet's cup and deck'd his dish !
Poor shadow cast from an unsteady wish,
Itself a substance by no other right
But that it intercepted Reason's light ;

It dimm'd his eye, it darken'd on his brow,
A peevish mood, a tedious time, I trow !
   Thank Heaven ! 'tis not so now.

O bliss of blissful hours !
The boon of Heaven's decreeing,
While yet in Eden's bowers
Dwelt the first husband and his sinless mate !
The one sweet plant, which, piteous Heaven
    agreeing,
They bore with them thro' Eden's closing gate !
Of life's gay summer tide the sovran rose !
Late autumn's amaranth, that more fragrant blows
When passion's flowers all fall or fade ;
If this were ever his, in outward being,
Or but his own true love's projected shade,
Now that at length by certain proof he knows,
That whether real or a magic show,
Whate'er it was, it is no longer so ;
Though heart be lonesome, hope laid low,
Yet, Lady ! deem him not unblest :
The certainty that struck hope dead,
Hath left contentment in her stead :
   And that is next to best !


## THE GARDEN OF BOCCACCIO.*

OF late, in one of those most weary hours,
   When life seems emptied of all genial powers,

---

* Printed in *The Keepsake*, Lond., 1829, to accompany a
drawing by Stothard.—ED.

A dreary mood, which he who ne'er has known
May bless his happy lot, I sate alone ;
And from the numbing spell to win relief,
Call'd on the past for thought of glee or grief.
In vain ! bereft alike of grief and glee,
I sate and cower'd o'er my own vacancy !
And as I watch'd the dull continuous ache,
Which, all else slumbering, seem'd alone to wake ;
O Friend ! long wont to notice yet conceal,
And soothe by silence what words cannot heal,
I but half saw that quiet hand of thine
Place on my desk this exquisite design.
Boccaccio's Garden and its faery,
The love, the joyaunce, and the gallantry !
An Idyll, with Boccaccio's spirit warm,
Framed in the silent poesy of form.
Like flocks adown a newly-bathed steep
Emerging from a mist ; or like a stream
Of music soft that not dispels the sleep,
But casts in happier moulds the slumberer's dream,
Gazed by an idle eye with silent might
The picture stole upon my inward sight.
A tremulous warmth crept gradual o'er my chest,
As though an infant's finger touch'd my breast.
And one by one (I know not whence) were brought
All spirits of power that most had stirr'd my      [thought
In selfless boyhood, on a new world tost
Of wonder, and in its own fancies lost ;
Or charm'd my youth, that, kindled from above,
Loved ere it loved, and sought a form for love ;
Or lent a lustre to the earnest scan
Of manhood, musing what and whence is man !

Wild strain of Scalds, that in the sea-worn caves
Rehearsed their war-spell to the winds and waves;
Or fateful hymn of those prophetic maids,
That call'd on Hertha in deep forest glades;
Or minstrel lay, that cheer'd the baron's feast;
Or rhyme of city pomp, of monk and priest,
Judge, mayor, and many a guild in long array,
To high-church pacing on the great saint's day.
And many a verse which to myself I sang,
That woke the tear yet stole away the pang,
Of hopes which in lamenting I renew'd.
And last, a matron now, of sober mien,
Yet radiant still and with no earthly sheen,
Whom as a faery child my childhood woo'd
Even in my dawn of thought—Philosophy;
Though then unconscious of herself, pardie,
She bore no other name than Poesy;
And, like a gift from heaven, in lifeful glee,
That had but newly left a mother's knee,
Prattled and play'd with bird and flower, and stone,
As if with elfin playfellows well known,
And life reveal'd to innocence alone.
Thanks, gentle artist! now I can descry
Thy fair creation with a mastering eye,
And all awake! And now in fix'd gaze stand,
Now wander through the Eden of thy hand;
Praise the green arches, on the fountain clear
See fragment shadows of the crossing deer;
And with that serviceable nymph I stoop
The crystal from its restless pool to scoop.
I see no longer! I myself am there,

Sit on the ground-sward, and the banquet share.
'Tis I, that sweep that lute's love-echoing strings,
And gaze upon the maid who gazing sings;
Or pause and listen to the tinkling bells
From the high tower, and think that there she dwells.
With old Boccaccio's soul I stand possesst,
And breathe an air like life, that swells my chest.

The brightness of the world, O thou once free,
And always fair, rare land of courtesy!
O Florence! with the Tuscan fields and hills
And famous Arno, fed with all their rills;
Thou brightest star of star-bright Italy!
Rich, ornate, populous, all treasures thine,
The golden corn, the olive, and the vine.
Fair cities, gallant mansions, castles old,
And forests, where beside his leafy hold
The sullen boar hath heard the distant horn,
And whets his tusks against the gnarled thorn;
Palladian palace with its storied halls;
Fountains, where Love lies listening to their falls;
Gardens, where flings the bridge its airy span,
And Nature makes her happy home with man;
Where many a gorgeous flower is duly fed
With its own rill, on its own spangled bed,
And wreathes the marble urn, or leans its head,
A mimic mourner, that with veil withdrawn
Weeps liquid gems, the presents of the dawn;—
Thine all delights, and every muse is thine;
And more than all, the embrace and intertwine
Of all with all in gay and twinkling dance!

Mid gods of Greece and warriors of romance,
See ! Boccace sits, unfolding on his knees
The new-found roll of old Mæonides ;*
But from his mantle's fold, and near the heart,
Peers Ovid's holy book of Love's sweet smart ! †
O all-enjoying and all-blending sage,
Long be it mine to con thy mazy page,
Where, half conceal'd, the eye of fancy views
Fauns, nymphs, and winged saints, all gracious to
    thy muse !

Still in thy garden let me watch their pranks,
And see in Dian's vest between the ranks
Of the trim vines, some maid that half believes
The vestal fires, of which her lover grieves,
With that sly satyr peeping through the leaves !

---

* Boccaccio claimed for himself the glory of having first
introduced the works of Homer to his countrymen.

† I know few more striking or more interesting proofs of
the overwhelming influence which the study of the Greek and
Roman classics exercised on the judgments, feelings, and
imaginations of the literati of Europe at the commencement
of the restoration of literature, than the passage in the *Filo-
copo* of Boccaccio, where the sage instructor, Racheo, as
soon as the young prince and the beautiful girl Biancofiore
had learned their letters, sets them to study the Holy Book,
Ovid's Art of Love. "Incominciò Racheo a mettere il suo
officio in esecuzione con intera sollecitudine. E loro, in breve
tempo, insegnato a conoscer le lettere, fece leggere il santo
libro d'Ovvidio, nel quale il sommo poeta mostra come i santi
fuochi di Venere si debbano ne' freddi cuori accendere."

## ON A CATARACT

FROM A CAVERN NEAR THE SUMMIT OF A
MOUNTAIN PRECIPICE.*

### STROPHE.

UNPERISHING youth !
   Thou leapest from forth
The cell of thy hidden nativity ;
Never mortal saw
The cradle of the strong one ;
Never mortal heard
The gathering of his voices ;
The deep murmur'd charm of the son of the rock,
That is lisp'd evermore at his slumberless fountain.
There's a cloud at the portal, a spray-woven veil
At the shrine of his ceaseless renewing ;
It embosoms the roses of dawn,
It entangles the shafts of the noon,
And into the bed of its stillness
The moonshine sinks down as in slumber,
That the son of the rock, that the nursling of heaven
May be born in a holy twilight !

### ANTISTROPHE.

The wild goat in awe
Looks up and beholds
Above thee the cliff inaccessible ;—

* An expansion of a German poem by Count Stolberg.—ED.

Thou at once full-born
Madden'st in thy joyance,
Whirlest, shatter'st, splitt'st,
Life invulnerable.


## A CHILD'S EVENING PRAYER.

ERE on my bed my limbs I lay,
　　God grant me grace my prayers to say:
O God ! preserve my mother dear
In strength and health for many a year ;
And, O ! preserve my father too,
And may I pay him reverence due ;
And may I my best thoughts employ
To be my parents' hope and joy ;
And O ! preserve my brothers both
From evil doings and from sloth,
And may we always love each other
Our friends, our father, and our mother :
And still, O Lord, to me impart
An innocent and grateful heart,
That after my last sleep I may
Awake to thy eternal day !　　　*Amen.*


## LOVE'S APPARITION AND EVANISHMENT.

### AN ALLEGORIC ROMANCE.

LIKE a lone Arab, old and blind,
　　Some caravan had left behind,

Who sits beside a ruin'd well,
    Where the shy sand-asps bask and swell ;
And now he hangs his aged head aslant,
And listens for a human sound—in vain !
And now the aid, which Heaven alone can grant,
Upturns his eyeless face from Heaven to gain ;—
Even thus, in vacant mood, one sultry hour,
Resting my eye upon a drooping plant,
With brow low-bent, within my garden-bower,
I sate upon the couch of camomile ;
And—whether 'twas a transient sleep, perchance,
Flitted across the idle brain, the while
I watch'd the sickly calm with aimless scope,
In my own heart ; or that, indeed a trance,
Turn'd my eye inward—thee, O genial Hope,
Love's elder sister ! thee did I behold,
Drest as a bridesmaid, but all pale and cold,
With roseless cheek, all pale and cold and dim,
    Lie lifeless at my feet !
And then came Love, a sylph in bridal trim,
    And stood beside my seat ;
She bent, and kiss'd her sister's lips,
    As she was wont to do ;—
Alas ! 'twas but a chilling breath
Woke just enough of life in death
    To make Hope die anew.

### L'ENVOY.

IN vain we supplicate the Powers above ;
    There is no resurrection for the Love
That, nursed in tenderest care, yet fades away
In the chill'd heart by gradual self-decay.

## LOVE, HOPE, AND PATIENCE IN EDUCATION.*

O'ER wayward childhood would'st thou hold firm
rule,
And sun thee in the light of happy faces ;
Love, Hope, and Patience, these must be thy graces,
And in thine own heart let them first keep school.
For as old Atlas on his broad neck places
Heaven's starry globe, and there sustains it ;—so
Do these upbear the little world below
Of Education,—Patience, Love, and Hope.
Methinks, I see them group'd in seemly show,
The straiten'd arms upraised, the palms aslope,
And robes that touching as adown they flow,
Distinctly blend, like snow emboss'd in snow.

O part them never ! If Hope prostrate lie,
        Love too will sink and die.
But Love is subtle, and doth proof derive
From her own life that Hope is yet alive ;
And bending o'er, with soul-transfusing eyes,
And the soft murmurs of the mother dove,
Wooes back the fleeting spirit, and half supplies ;—
Thus Love repays to Hope what Hope first gave to
Love.

* Printed in *The Keepsake*, 1830, with the following title :—
" The Poet's Answer to a Lady's Question respecting the accom-
plishments most desirable in an instructress of children."

Yet haply there will come a weary day,
   When overtask'd at length
Both Love and Hope beneath the load give way.
Then with a statue's smile, a statue's strength,
Stands the mute sister, Patience, nothing loth,
And both supporting does the work of both.


## A CHARACTER.

A BIRD, who for his other sins
  Had lived amongst the Jacobins ;
Though like a kitten amid rats,
Or callow tit in nest of bats,
He much abhorr'd all democrats ;
Yet nathless stood in ill report
Of wishing ill to Church and Court,
Though he'd nor claw, nor tooth, nor sting,
And learnt to pipe God save the King ;
Though each day did new feathers bring,
All swore he had a leathern wing ;
Nor polish'd wing, nor feather'd tail,
Nor down-clad thigh would aught avail ;
And though—his tongue devoid of gall—
He civilly assured them all :—
" A bird am I of Phœbus' breed,
And on the sunflower cling and feed ;
My name, good sirs, is Thomas Tit !"
The bats would hail him brother cit,
Or, at the furthest, cousin-german.
At length the matter to determine,

He publicly denounced the vermin;
He spared the mouse, he praised the owl;
But bats were neither flesh nor fowl.
Blood-sucker, vampire, harpy, goul,
Came in full clatter from his throat,
Till his old nest-mates changed their note
To hireling, traitor, and turncoat,—
A base apostate who had sold
His very teeth and claws for gold;—
And then his feathers!—sharp the jest—
No doubt he feather'd well his nest!
A Tit indeed! ay, tit for tat—
With place and title, brother Bat,
We soon shall see how well he'll play
Count Goldfinch, or Sir Joseph Jay!"

Alas, poor Bird! and ill-bestarr'd—
Or rather let us say, poor Bard!
And henceforth quit the allegoric,
With metaphor and simile,
For simple facts and style historic:—
Alas, poor Bard! no gold had he.
Behind another's team he stept,
And plough'd and sow'd, while others reapt;
The work was his, but theirs the glory,
*Sic vos non vobis,* his whole story.
Besides, whate'er he wrote or said
Came from his heart as well as head;
And though he never left in lurch
His king, his country, or his church,
'Twas but to humour his own cynical
Contempt of doctrines Jacobinical;

To his own conscience only hearty,
'Twas but by chance he served the party ;—
The self-same things had said and writ,
Had Pitt been Fox, and Fox been Pitt ;
Content his own applause to win,
Would never dash through thick and thin,
And he can make, so say the wise,
No claim who makes no sacrifice ;—
And Bard still less :—what claim had he,
Who swore it vex'd his soul to see
So grand a cause, so proud a realm,
With Goose and Goody at the helm ;
Who long ago had fall'n asunder
But for their rivals' baser blunder,
The coward whine and Frenchified
Slaver and slang of the other side !—

  Thus, his own whim his only bribe,
Our Bard pursued his old A. B. C.
Contented if he could subscribe
In fullest sense his name Ἔστησε ;
('Tis Punic Greek for ' he hath stood !')
Whate'er the men, the cause was good ;
And therefore with a right good will,
Poor fool, he fights their battles still.
Tush ! squeak'd the Bats ;—a mere bravado
To whitewash that base renegado ;
'Tis plain unless you're blind or mad,
His conscience for the bays he barters ;—
And true it is—as true as sad—

These circlets of green baize he had—
But then, alas ! they were his garters !
    Ah ! silly Bard, unfed, untended,
His lamp but glimmer'd in its socket ;
He lived unhonour'd and unfriended
With scarce a penny in his pocket ;—
Nay—tho' he hid it from the many—
With scarce a pocket for his penny !


## THE REPROOF AND REPLY.

" FIE, Mr. Coleridge !—and can this be you ?
        Break two commandments ? and in church-
            time too !
Have you not heard, or have you heard in vain,
The birth and parentage-recording strain ?
Confessions shrill, that out-shrill'd mackarel drown—
Fresh from the drop, the youth not yet cut down.
Letter to sweet-heart—the last dying speech—
And didn't all this begin in Sabbath-breach ?
You, that knew better ! In broad open day,
Steal in, steal out, and steal our flowers away ?
What could possess you ? Ah ! sweet youth, I fear
The chap with horns and tail was at your ear !"


Such sounds of late, accusing fancy brought
From fair —— to the Poet's thought.
Now hear the meek Parnassian youth's reply :—
A bow, a pleading look, a downcast eye,—
And then :
            " Fair dame ! a visionary wight,

Hard by your hill-side mansion sparkling white,
His thoughts all hovering round the Muses' home,
Long hath it been your poet's wont to roam,
And many a morn, on his becharmed sense
So rich a stream of music issued thence,
He deem'd himself, as it flow'd warbling on,
Beside the vocal fount of Helicon !
But when, as if to settle the concern,
A nymph too he beheld, in many a turn,
Guiding the sweet rill from its fontal urn,—
Say, can you blame ? — No ! none that saw and
      heard
Could blame a bard, that he thus inly stirr'd ;
A muse beholding in each fervent trait,
Took Mary —— for Polly Hymnia !
Or haply as there stood beside the maid
One loftier form in sable stole array'd,
If with regretful thought he hail'd in thee
——, his long-lost friend, Mol Pomene !
But most of you, soft warblings, I complain !
'Twas ye that from the bee-hive of my brain
Lured the wild fancies forth, a freakish rout,
And witch'd the air with dreams turn'd inside out.

Thus all conspired—each power of eye and ear,
And this gay month, th' enchantress of the year,
To cheat poor me (no conjuror, God wot !)
And ——'s self accomplice in the plot.
Can you then wonder if I went astray ?
Not bards alone, nor lovers mad as they ;—
All Nature day-dreams in the month of May.

And if I pluck'd each flower that sweetest blows,—
Who walks in sleep, needs follow must his nose.
Thus, long accustom'd on the twy-fork'd hill,
To pluck both flower and floweret at my will;
The garden's maze, like No-man's-land, I tread,
Nor common law, nor statute in my head;
For my own proper smell, sight, fancy, feeling,
With autocratic hand at once repealing
Five Acts of Parliament 'gainst private stealing!
But yet from —— who despairs of grace?
There's no spring-gun or man-trap in that face!
Let Moses then look black, and Aaron blue,
That look as if they had little else to do:
For —— speaks, "Poor youth! he's but a waif!
The spoons all right? the hen and chickens safe?
Well, well, he shall not forfeit our regards—
The Eighth Commandment was not made for
　　　Bards!"


## CHOLERA CURED BEFORE-HAND.

Or a premonition promulgated gratis for the use of the Useful Classes, specially those resident in St. Giles's, Saffron Hill, Bethnal Green, &c.; and likewise, inasmuch as the good man is merciful even to the beasts, for the benefit of the Bulls and Bears of the Stock Exchange.

PAINS ventral, subventral,
　　In stomach or entrail,
Think no longer mere prefaces
For grins, groans, and wry faces;

But off to the doctor, fast as ye can crawl !—
Yet far better 'twould be not to have them at all.

Now to 'scape inward aches,
Eat no plums nor plum-cakes ;
Cry avaunt ! new potato—
And don't drink, like old Cato.
Ah ! beware of Dispipsy,
And don't ye get tipsy !
For tho' gin and whiskey
May make you feel frisky,
They're but crimps to Dispipsy ;
And nose to tail, with this gipsy
Comes, black as a porpus,
The diabolus ipse,
Call'd Cholery Morpus ;
Who with horns, hoofs, and tail, croaks for carrion
      to feed him,
Tho' being a Devil, no one never has seed him !

Ah ! then my dear honies,
There's no cure for you
For loves nor for monies :—
You'll find it too true.
Och ! the hallabaloo !
Och ! och ! how you'll wail,
When the offal-fed vagrant
Shall turn you as blue
As the gas-light unfragrant,
That gushes in jets from beneath his own tail ;—
'Till swift as the mail,

He at last brings the cramps on,
That will twist you like Samson.
So without further blethring,
Dear mudlarks ! my brethren !
Of all scents and degrees,
(Yourselves and your shes)
Forswear all cabal, lads,
Wakes, unions, and rows,
Hot dreams, and cold salads,
And don't pig in styes that would suffocate sows !
Quit Cobbett's, O'Connell's and Beelzebub's
       banners,
And whitewash at once bowels, rooms, hands, and
       manners !

## COLOGNE.

IN Köhln, a town of monks and bones,
    And pavements fang'd with murderous stones,
And rags, and hags, and hideous wenches ;
I counted two and seventy stenches,
All well defined, and several stinks !
Ye Nymphs that reign o'er sewers and sinks,
The river Rhine, it is well known,
Doth wash your city of Cologne ;
But tell me, Nymphs ! what power divine
Shall henceforth wash the river Rhine ?

## ON MY JOYFUL DEPARTURE
### FROM THE SAME CITY.

    As I am rhymer,
And now at least a merry one,

Mr. Mum's Rudesheimer
And the church of St. Geryon
Are the two things alone
That deserve to be known
In the body and soul-stinking town of Cologne.


## WRITTEN IN AN ALBUM.

PARRY seeks the polar ridge ;
    Rhymes seeks S. T. Coleridge,
Author of works, whereof—though not in Dutch—
The public little knows—the publisher too much.


## METRICAL FEET.

### LESSON FOR A BOY.

TRŌCHĔE trĭps frŏm lōng tŏ shŏrt ;
    From long to long in solemn sort
Slōw Spōndēe stālks ; strōng fōot ! yet ill able
Ĕvĕr tŏ cōme ŭp wĭth Dāctўl trĭsyllăblĕ.
Ĭāmbĭcs mārch frŏm shŏrt tŏ lōng ;—
Wĭth ă lēap ănd ă bōund thĕ swĭft Ānăpæsts thrōng ;
One syllable long, with one short at each side,
Ămphībrăchўs hāstes wĭth ă stātelў stride ;—
Fĭrst ănd lāst beĭng lōng, mĭddlĕ shŏrt, Āmphĭ-
    mācer
Strīkes hĭs thūndērĭng hoofs līke ă prōud hĭgh-
    brĕd Rācer.
If Derwent be innocent, steady, and wise,
And delight in the things of earth, water, and skies ;

Tender warmth at his heart, with these metres to
 show it,
With sound sense in his brains, may make Derwent
 a poet,—
May crown him with fame, and must win him the
 love
Of his father on earth and his Father above.
     My dear, dear child !
Could you stand upon Skiddaw, you would not
 from its whole ridge
See a man who so loves you as your fond S. T.
 COLERIDGE.


## THE HOMERIC HEXAMETER

### DESCRIBED AND EXEMPLIFIED.*

STRONGLY it bears us along in swelling and
 limitless billows,
Nothing before and nothing behind but the sky
 and the Ocean.


## THE OVIDIAN ELEGIAC METRE

### DESCRIBED AND EXEMPLIFIED.*

IN the hexameter rises the fountain's silvery column ;
In the pentameter aye falling in melody back.


* Translated from Schiller.   Printed in *Friendship's Offer-
ing*, 1834.

## TO THE YOUNG ARTIST,

### KAYSER OF KASERWERTH.

KAYSER ! to whom, as to a second self,
    Nature, or Nature's next-of-kin, the Elf,
Hight Genius, hath dispensed the happy skill
To cheer or soothe the parting friend's Alas !
Turning the blank scroll to a magic glass,
That makes the absent present at our will ;
And to the shadowing of thy pencil gives
Such seeming substance, that it almost lives.

Well hast thou given the thoughtful Poet's face !
Yet hast thou on the tablet of his mind
A more delightful portrait left behind—
Even thy own youthful beauty, and artless grace,
Thy natural gladness and eyes bright with glee !
        Kayser ! farewell !
Be wise ! be happy ! and forget not me.
    1833.

## JOB'S LUCK.*

SLY Beelzebub took all occasions
    To try Job's constancy and patience ;
He took his honours, took his health,
He took his children, took his wealth,
His camels, horses, asses, cows—
And the sly Devil did not take his spouse.

* Printed in *The Morning Post*, Sept. 26, 1801, with the
title of *The Devil Outwitted ;* and somewhat differently in *The
Keepsake* for 1829.

But Heaven that brings out good from evil,
And loves to disappoint the Devil,
Had predetermined to restore
Twofold all Job had before,
His children, camels, horses, cows,—
Short-sighted Devil, not to take his spouse !


## ON AN INSIGNIFICANT.

'TIS Cypher lies beneath this crust—
Whom Death created into dust.


## PROFUSE KINDNESS.

Νήπιοι οὐκ ἴσασιν ὅσῳ πλέον ἥμισυ πάντος.—*Hesiod.*

WHAT a spring-tide of Love to dear friends in
a shoal !
Half of it to one were worth double the whole!


## CHARITY IN THOUGHT.

TO praise men as good, and to take them for such,
Is a grace, which no soul can mete out to a
tittle ;—
Of which he who has not a little too much,
Will by Charity's gauge surely have much too
little.

# A THOUGHT SUGGESTED BY A VIEW

## OF SADDLEBACK IN CUMBERLAND.*

ON stern Blencartha's perilous height
    The winds are tyrannous and strong ;
And flashing forth unsteady light
From stern Blencartha's skiey height,
    As loud the torrents throng !
Beneath the moon, in gentle weather,
They bind the earth and sky together.
But oh ! the sky and all its forms, how quiet !
The things that seek the earth, how full of noise
      and riot !

## SONG, *EX IMPROVISO,*

### ON HEARING A SONG IN PRAISE OF A
### LADY'S BEAUTY. †

'TIS not the lily brow I prize,
    Nor roseate cheeks nor sunny eyes,
    Enough of lilies and of roses !
A thousand fold more dear to me
The look that gentle Love discloses,—
    That look which Love alone can see.

*Ἔρως ἀεὶ λάληδρος ἕταιρος.*

IN many ways doth the full heart reveal
    The presence of the love it would conceal ;

---

* *The Amulet,* 1833.      † *The Keepsake,* 1830.

But in far more th' estranged heart lets know
The absence of the love which yet it fain would
   show.

## WHAT IS LIFE ? *

RESEMBLES life what once was deem'd of
      Too ample in itself for human sight ?   [light,
An absolute self—an element ungrounded—
All that we see, all colours of all shade
         By encroach of darkness made ?—
Is very life by consciousness unbounded ?
And all the thoughts, pains, joys of mortal breath,
A war-embrace of wrestling life and death ?

## HUMILITY THE MOTHER OF CHARITY.

FRAIL creatures are we all !   To be the best,
      Is but the fewest faults to have :—
Look thou then to thyself, and leave the rest
      To God, thy conscience, and the grave.

## ON AN INFANT

### WHICH DIED BEFORE BAPTISM.

" BE, rather than be call'd, a child of God,"
         Death whisper'd !—with assenting nod,
Its head upon its mother's breast,

---

* *The Literary Souvenir*, 1829.

The Baby bow'd, without demur—
Of the kingdom of the Blest
  Possessor, not inheritor.


*—E cœlo descendit* γνῶθι σεαυτόν.*—Juvenal.*

Γνῶθι σεαυτόν !—and is this the prime
And heaven-sprung adage of the olden time !—
Say, canst thou make thyself ?—Learn first that
    trade ;—
Haply thou mayst know what thyself had made.
What hast thou, Man, that thou darest call thine
    own ?—
What is there in thee, Man, that can be known ?—
Dark fluxion, all unfixable by thought,
A phantom dim of past and future wrought,
Vain sister of the worm,—life, death, soul, clod—
Ignore thyself, and strive to know thy God !


*Beareth all things.*—2 Cor. xiii. 7.

GENTLY I took that which ungently came,
  And without scorn forgave :—Do thou the
    same.
A wrong done to thee think a cat's-eye spark
Thou wouldst not see, were not thine own heart
    dark.
Thine own keen sense of wrong that thirsts for sin,
Fear that—the spark self-kindled from within,

Which blown upon will blind thee with its glare,
Or smother'd stifle thee with noisome air.
Clap on the extinguisher, pull up the blinds,
And soon the ventilated spirit finds
Its natural daylight.   If a foe have kenn'd,
Or worse than foe, an alienated friend,
A rib of dry rot in thy ship's stout side,
Think it God's message, and in humble pride
With heart of oak replace it ;—thine the gains—
Give him the rotten timber for his pains !


## MY BAPTISMAL BIRTH-DAY.*

GOD'S child in Christ adopted,—Christ my all,—
What that earth boasts were not lost cheaply,
        rather
Than forfeit that blest name, by which I call
The Holy One, the Almighty God, my Father ?—
Father ! in Christ we live, and Christ in Thee—
Eternal Thou, and everlasting we.
The heir of heaven, henceforth I fear not death :
In Christ I live ! in Christ I draw the breath
Of the true life !—Let then earth, sea, and sky
Make war against me ! On my front I show
Their mighty master's seal.   In vain they try
To end my life, that can but end its woe.—
Is that a death-bed where a Christian lies ?—
Yes ! but not his—'tis Death itself there dies.


* These are presumably the verses recited by Coleridge to
Emerson when the latter made a pilgrimage to Highgate on

Τό τοι 'ΕΣΤΗΣΕ τοῦ ἐπιδανοῦς Epitaphium testamentarium αὐτόγραφον.

Quœ linquam, aut nihil, aut nihili, aut vix sunt mea.
    Sordes
Do Morti : reddo cætera, Christe ! tibi.*

## EPITAPH.

STOP, Christian passer-by !—Stop, child of God,
    And read with gentle breast.  Beneath this sod
A poet lies, or that which once seem'd he.—
O, lift one thought in prayer for S. T. C. ;
That he who many a year with toil of breath
Found death in life, may here find life in death !
Mercy for praise—to be forgiven for fame
He ask'd, and hoped, through Christ.  Do thou
        the same !

*9th November,* 1833.

August 5, 1833. " When I rose to go, he said, ' I do not
know whether you care about poetry, but I will repeat some
verses I lately made on my baptismal anniversary,' and he
recited with strong emphasis, standing, ten or twelve lines,
beginning, ' Born unto God in Christ—'"—ENGLISH TRAITS,
§ 1, *First Visit to England.*

* *Literary Souvenir,* 1827.

# SUPPLEMENT

# SUPPLEMENT.

## MONODY ON THE DEATH OF CHATTERTON.

### (ORIGINAL VERSION.)*

[This poem has since appeared in print, much altered, whether for the better I doubt. This was, I believe, written before the Author went to College. (Note by J. T. C.)]

NOW prompts the Muse poetic lays,
    And high my bosom beats with love of praise,
But, *Chatterton!* methinks I hear thy name,
For cold my fancy grows, and dead each hope of
    Fame.

When Want and cold Neglect had chill'd thy soul,
Athirst for Death I see thee drain the bowl,
    Thy corse of many a livid hue
    On the bare ground I view,

* This original draught of Coleridge's Monody on Chatterton appears to have been produced at Christ's Hospital as a school exercise, together with the two following Poems. It is derived from a note-book in the handwriting of the late Sir John Taylor Coleridge, the nephew of the poet, kept at Eton College in 1807, which has been kindly placed at the publisher's disposal by his son, the present Lord Coleridge, of Ottery St. Mary.

While various passions all my mind engage :
Now is my breast distended with a sigh,
  And now a flash of rage
Darts through the tear that glistens in my eye.

Is *this* the land of liberal heart?
Is *this* the land where Genius ne'er in vain
Pour'd forth her soul-enchanting strain ?
Ah me ! yet *Butler* 'gainst the bigot foe
Well skill'd to aim keen humour's dart,
Yet Butler felt want's poignant sting ;
And *Otway*, master of the Tragic art,
Whom Pity's self had bade to sing,
Sunk beneath the load of woe
Which can the *generous* Briton ever hear
And starts not in his eye the indignant tear ?
  Elate of Heart, and confident of fame
From vales, where Avon sports, the minstrel came.
  Gay as the Poet hastes along
  He meditates the future song,
How Ælla battled with his country's foes—
  And while Fancy in the air
  Paints him many a vision fair,
His eyes dance rapture, and his bosom glows !
With generous joy he views the rising gold,
  He listens* to many a widow's prayers,
  And many an orphan's thanks he hears—
  He soothes to peace the care-worn breast,
  He bids the debtor's eyes know rest,
  And liberty, and bliss behold.

   * *Sic* in MS.   Qy. "lists."—ED.

And now he punishes the heart of steel
And her own iron rod he makes oppression feel.
Fated to heave sad Disappointment's sigh,
To feel the hope now raised and now deprest,
With all the burnings of an injured breast.
Lo ! from thy dark Fate's sorrow keen
In vain, O youth, I turn th' affrighted eye.
     For busy Fancy ever nigh
The hateful picture forces on my sight !
     There, death of every dear delight,
     Frowns Poverty of giant mien !
In vain I seek the charms of youthful grace,
Thy sunken eye, thy haggard cheek she shows,
The quick emotions struggling in thy face
     Faint index of thy mental throes,
When each strong passion spurn'd control,
And not a friend was nigh to calm thy stormy soul.
     Such was the sad and gloomy hour
     When anguish'd Care of sullen brow
Prepared the poison's death-cold power.
Already to thy lips was raised the bowl
When filial Pity stood thee by,—
The fixed eye she bade thee roll
On scenes which well might melt thy soul—
     Thy native cot she held to view,
     Thy native cot, where Peace ere long
     Had listen'd to thy evening song.
Thy sister's *shrieks* she bade thee hear,
And mark thy mother's thrilling tear.
She bade thee feel her deep-drawn sigh,
     And all her *silent* agony of woe.

" And from *thy* fate shall such distress ensue ?
" Ah, dash the poison'd chalice from thy hand."
And thou hadst dash'd it, at her soft command,
But that Despair and Indignation rose,
And told again the story of thy woes,
Told the keen insult of the unfeeling heart.
The dread dependence on the low-born mind,
Told every woe, for which thy breast might smart,
Neglect and grinning Scorn and Want combined—
Recoiling back thou badest the friend of Pain
Quick roll a tide of Death through every icening
    vein.

        O Spirit blest !
Whether the Eternal's throne around,
Amidst the blaze of Seraphim,
Thou pourest forth the grateful hymn
Or soaring through the blest Domain
Enrapturest Angels with thy strain,
Grant me, like thee, the lyre to sound,
Like thee with fire divine to glow,
Like thee, when rage the waves of woe,
To leave behind contempt and want and state
And seek in other worlds an happier fate.*

   * It seems that the Author considered the sentiment in these
last three lines "so improper," that he soon altered them to
those that now stand in the text.   (See vol. i. pp. 60-61.)
The first foot-note on p. 61 should be deleted.

## TO THE EVENING STAR.\*

O MEEK attendant of Sol's setting blaze,
    I hail, sweet star, thy chaste effulgent glow ;
On thee full oft with fixed eye I gaze
    Till I, methinks, all spirit seem to grow.

O first and fairest of the starry choir,
    O loveliest 'mid the daughters of the night,
Must not the maid I love like thee inspire
    *Pure* joy and *calm* Delight ?

Must she not be, as is thy placid sphere
    Serenely brilliant ?   Whilst to gaze a while
Be all my wish 'mid Fancy's high career
    E'en till she quit this scene of earthly toil ;
Then Hope perchance might fondly sigh to join
Her spirit in thy kindred orb, O star benign !


## ANNA AND HARLAND.†

W ITHIN these wilds was Anna wont to rove
    While Harland told his love in many a sigh,
    But stern on Harland rolled her brother's eye,
They fought, they fell—her brother and her love !

* Now first printed from the late Sir J. T. Coleridge's MS.
book.

    † Now first printed from the late Sir J. T. Coleridge's MS.
note-book.

To Death's dark house did grief-worn Anna haste,
    Yet here her pensive ghost delights to stay ;
    Oft pouring on the winds the broken lay—
And hark, I hear her—'twas the passing blast.

I love to sit upon her tomb's dark grass,
    Then Memory backward rolls Time's shadowy
       tide ;
    The tales of other days before me glide :
With eager thought I seize them as they pass ;
For fair, though faint, the forms of Memory gleam,
Like Heaven's bright beauteous bow reflected in
    the stream.*


## TRANSLATION OF WRANGHAM'S

*Hendecasyllabi ad Bruntonam e Granta Exituram.*†

MAID of unboastful charms ! whom white-robed
    Truth
Right onward guiding through the maze of youth,
Forbade the Circe Praise to witch thy soul ;
And dash'd to earth th' intoxicating bowl :

* The last two lines were transferred to another poem printed in *The Watchman.* (See Vol. i. pp. 66-67.)

† Printed in a small volume of "Poems by Francis Wrangham, M.A., Member of Trinity College, Cambridge, Lond. 1795, pp. 79-83, where the original Hendecasyllables will be found. This translation was sent to Miss Brunton, sister of the Lady (Mrs. Merry) who was the subject of the original verses, with the lines that follow it in the text.

The meek-eyed Pity, eloquently fair,
Clasp'd to a bosom with a mother's care;
And, as she loved thy kindred form to trace,
The slow smile wander'd o'er her pallid face.

For never yet did mortal voice impart
Tones more congenial to the sadden'd heart:
Whether, to rouse the sympathetic glow,
Thou pourest lone Monimia's tale of woe;
Or haply clothest with funereal vest
The bridal loves that wept in Juliet's breast.
O'er our chill limbs the thrilling Terrors creep,
Th' entranced Passions their still vigil keep;
While the deep sighs, responsive to the song,
Sound through the silence of the trembling throng.

But purer raptures lighten'd from thy face,
And spread o'er all thy form an holier grace,
When from the daughter's breast the father drew
The life he gave, and mix'd the big tear's dew.
Nor was it thine th' heroic strain to roll
With mimic feelings foreign from the soul:
Bright in thy parent's eye we mark'd the tear;
Methought he said, " Thou art no Actress here!
"A semblance of thyself the *Grecian* dame,
" And Brunton and Euphrasia still the same!"

O soon to seek the city's busier scene,
Pause thee a while, thou chaste-eyed maid serene,
Till Granta's sons from all her sacred bowers
With grateful hand shall weave Pierian flowers
To twine a fragrant chaplet round thy brow,
Enchanting ministress of virtuous woe!

## TO MISS BRUNTON,

WITH THE PRECEDING TRANSLATION.*

THAT darling of the Tragic Muse—
　　When Wrangham sung her praise,
Thalia lost her rosy hues
　　And sicken'd at his lays :

But transient was th' unwonted sigh ;
　　For soon the Goddess spied
A sister form of mirthful eye
　　And danced for joy and cried :

" Meek Pity's sweetest child, proud dame,
　　The fates have given to you !
Still bid your Poet boast her name ;
　　*I* have *my* Brunton too."

## THE MAD MONK.†

I HEARD a voice from Etna's side ;
　　Where, o'er a cavern's mouth
　　That fronted to the south
A chestnut spread its umbrage wide :
A hermit, or a monk, the man might be ;
　　But him I could not see :
And thus the music flow'd along,
In melody most like to old Sicilian song :

* Printed in *Wrangham's Poems,* 1795, p. 83, *note.*

† Printed in *The Wild Wreath,* edited by M. E. Robinson.
Lond. Rich. Phillips, 1804, 8vo, pp. 142-144.

" There was a time when earth, and sea, and skies,
    The bright green vale, and forest's dark recess,
With all things, lay before mine eyes
    In steady loveliness :
But now I feel, on earth's uneasy scene,
    Such sorrows as will never cease ;—
    I only ask for peace ;
If I must live to know that such a time has been ! "
    A silence then ensued :
        Till from the cavern came
        A voice ; it was the same !
And thus, in mournful tone, its dreary plaint re-
    newed :—

" Last night, as o'er the sloping turf I trod,
    The smooth green turf, to me a vision gave
Beneath mine eyes, the sod—
    The roof of Rosa's grave !
My heart has need with dreams like these to strive,
    For, when I woke, beneath mine eyes I found
    The plot of mossy ground,
On which we oft have sat when Rosa was alive.—
    Why must the rock, and margin of the flood,
    Why must the hills so many flowerets bear,
Whose colours to a *murder'd* maiden's blood
    Such sad resemblance wear ?—

" *I struck the wound,*—this hand of mine !
For oh, thou maid divine,
    I loved to agony !
The youth whom thou call'd'st thine
    Did never love like me ?

" Is it the stormy clouds above
    That flashed so red a gleam?
    On yonder downward trickling stream?—
'Tis not the blood of her I love.—
The sun torments me from his western bed :
    Oh, let him cease for ever to diffuse
    Those crimson spectre hues !
Oh, let me lie in peace, and be for ever dead ! "
Here ceased the voice.   In deep dismay,
Down thro' the forest I pursued my way.

# APPENDIX.

# APPENDIX.

## THE OLD MAN OF THE ALPS.*

[The poem of *Lewti* appeared in *The Morning Post* of April 13, 1798 (*vide supra*, p. 100), with the signature of "Nicias Erythræus." The same signature had been previously appended to the following poem, entitled 'The Old Man of the Alps,' which appeared in the number for March 8, 1798. This seems to be strong presumptive evidence in favour of Coleridge's authorship, in the absence of any other claimant; but as Coleridge never otherwise owned the production, and there exists no collateral proof, we have thought it better to relegate it to the Appendix.—Ed.]

STRANGER! whose eyes a look of pity show,
　　Say, will you listen to a tale of woe?
A tale in no unwonted horrors drest;
But sweet is pity to an aged breast.
This voice did falter with old age before;
Sad recollections make it falter more.
Beside the torrent and beneath a wood
High in these Alps my summer cottage stood;
One daughter still remain'd to cheer my way,
The evening-star of life's declining day;
Duly she hied to fill her milking-pail
Ere shout of herdsman rang from cliff or vale;
When she return'd, before the summer shiel,
On the fresh grass she spread the dairy meal;
Just as the snowy peaks began to lose
In glittering silver lights their rosy hues.

* *Morning Post*, March 8, 1798.

Singing in woods or bounding o'er the lawn
No blither creature hail'd the early dawn;
And if I spoke of hearts by pain oppress'd
When every friend is gone to them that rest,
Or of old men that leave, when they expire,
Daughters that should have perish'd with their sire—
Leave them to toil all day through paths unknown
And house at night behind some sheltering stone;
Impatient of the thought, with lively cheer
She broke half closed the tasteless tale severe.
*She* play'd with fancies of a gayer hue,
Enamour'd of the scenes her *wishes* drew;
And oft she prattled with an eager tongue
Of promised joys that would not loiter long,
Till with her tearless eyes so bright and fair
She seem'd to see them realized in air!
In fancy oft, within some sunny dell,
Where never wolf should howl or tempest yell,
She built a little home of joy and rest,
And fill'd it with the friends whom she loved best:
She named the inmates of her fancied cot,
And gave to each his own peculiar lot;
Which with our little herd abroad should roam,
And which should tend the dairy's toil at home;
And now the hour approach'd which should restore
Her lover from the wars, to part no more.
Her whole frame flutter'd with uneasy joy;
I long'd myself to clasp the valiant boy;
And though I strove to calm *her* eager mood,
It was my own sole thought in solitude.
I told it to the Saints amid my hymns—
For O! you know not on an old man's limbs
How thrillingly the pleasant sunbeams play
That shine upon his daughter's wedding-day.

I hoped that those fierce tempests soon to rave
Unheard, unfelt, around *my* mountain grave,
Not undelightfully would break *her* rest,
While she lay pillow'd on her lover's breast,
Or join'd his pious prayer for pilgrims driven
Out to the mercy of the winds of heaven.
Yes ! now the hour approach'd that should restore
Her lover from the wars to part no more.
Her thoughts were wild, her soul was in her eye,
She wept and laugh'd as if she knew not why;
And she had made a song about the wars,
And sang it to the sun and to the stars !
But while she look'd and listen'd, stood and ran,
And saw him plain in every distant man,
By treachery stabb'd, on Nansy's murderous day,
A senseless corse th' expected husband lay.
A wounded man who met us in the wood
Heavily ask'd her where *my* cottage stood,
And told us all : she cast her eyes around
As if his words had been but empty sound ;
Then look'd to Heaven, like one that would deny
That such a thing *could be* beneath the sky.
*Again* he ask'd her if she knew my name,
And instantly an anguish wrench'd her frame
And left her mind imperfect.   No delight
Thenceforth she found in any cheerful sight,
Not even in those time-haunted wells and groves,
Scenes of past joy and birthplace of her loves.
If to her spirit any sound was dear
'Twas the deep moan that spoke the tempest near ;
Or sighs which chasms of icy vales outbreathe
Sent from the dark, imprison'd floods beneath.
She wander'd up the crag and down the slope,
But not, as in her happy days of hope,

To seek the churning-plant of sovereign power
That grew in clefts and bore a scarlet flower !
She roam'd without a purpose, all alone,
Thro' high grey vales unknowing and unknown.
     Kind-hearted stranger ! patiently you hear
A tedious tale : I thank you for that tear.
May never other tears o'ercloud your eye
Than those which gentle Pity can supply !
Did you not mark a towering convent hang
Where the huge rocks with sounds of torrents rang?
Even yet, methinks, its spiry turrets swim
Amid yon purple gloom ascending dim !
For thither oft would my poor child repair
To ease her soul by penitence and prayer.
I knew that peace at good men's prayers returns
Home to the contrite heart of him that mourns,
And check'd her not ; and often there she found
A timely pallet when the evening frown'd.
And there I trusted that my child would light
On shelter and on food, one dreadful night,
When there was uproar in the element
And she was absent.   To my rest I went :
I thought her safe, yet often did I wake
And felt my very heart within me ache.
No daughter near me, at this very door
Next morn I listen'd to the dying roar.
Above, below, the prowling vulture wail'd,
And down the cliffs the heavy vapour sail'd.
Up by the wide-spread waves in fury torn
Homestalls and pines along the vale were borne.
The Dalesmen in thick crowds appear'd below
Clearing the road, o'erwhelm'd with hills of snow.
At times to the proud gust's ascending swell
A pack of bloodhounds flung their doleful yell :

For after nights of storm that dismal train
The pious convent sends, with hope humane
To find some outstretch'd man—perchance to save,
Or give, at least, that last good gift, a grave !
But now a gathering crowd did I survey
That slowly up the pasture bent their way ;
Nor could I doubt but that their care had found
Some pilgrim in th' unchannell'd torrent drown'd.
And down the lawn I hasten'd to implore
That they would bring the body to my door ;
But soon exclaim'd a boy, who ran before,
" Thrown by the last night's waters from their bed
" Your daughter has been found, and she is dead ! ''

The old man paused.   May he who, sternly just,
Lays at his will his creatures in the dust ;
Some ere the earliest buds of hope be blown,
And some when every bloom of joy is flown ;
May he the parent to his child restore
In that unchanging realm where Love reigns evermore.
                              NICIAS ERYTHRÆUS.

----

## POEMS AND POETICAL FRAGMENTS.*

*Vivamus, mea Lesbia, atque amemus.*   CATULLUS.

MY LESBIA, let us love and live,
    And to the winds, my Lesbia, give
Each cold restraint, each boding fear
Of age, and all its saws severe !

* *Literary Remains of S.T.C.*, Lond., William Pickering,
1836, vol. i. pp. 274-281.  Communicated, with the exception
of the four last pieces, by Mr. Gutch.  The first piece (signed
' Mortimer ') appeared in *The Morning Post* of April 11, 1798.

Yon sun now posting to the main
Will set,—but 'tis to rise again;—
But we, when once our little light
Is set, must sleep in endless night.
Then come, with whom alone I'll live,
A thousand kisses take and give!
Another thousand!—to the store
Add hundreds—then a thousand more!
And when they to a million mount,
Let confusion take the account,—
That you, the number never knowing,
May continue still bestowing—
That I for joys may never pine,
Which never can again be mine!

------

*Lugete, O Veneres, Cupidinesque.* CATULLUS.

Pity, mourn in plaintive tone
The lovely starling dead and gone!
Pity mourns in plaintive tone
The lovely starling dead and gone.
Weep, ye Loves! and Venus, weep
The lovely starling fall'n asleep!
Venus sees with tearful eyes—
In her lap the starling lies,
While the Loves all in a ring
Softly stroke the stiffen'd wing.

------

*Moriens superstiti.*

" The hour-bell sounds, and I must go;
Death waits—again I hear him calling;—
No cowardly desires have I,
Nor will I shun his face appalling.
I die in faith and honour rich—

But ah ! I leave behind my treasure
In widowhood and lonely pain ;—
To live were surely then a pleasure !

" My lifeless eyes upon thy face
Shall never open more to-morrow ;
To-morrow shall thy beauteous eyes
Be closed to love, and drown'd in sorrow ;
To-morrow death shall freeze this hand,
And on thy breast, my wedded treasure,
I never, never more shall live ;—
Alas ! I quit a life of pleasure."

------

*Morienti superstes.*

" Yet art thou happier far than she
  Who feels the widow's love for thee !
For while her days are days of weeping,
Thou, in peace, in silence sleeping,
In some still world, unknown, remote,
  The mighty parent's care hast found,
Without whose tender guardian thought
  No sparrow falleth to the ground."

------

'Twas sweet to know it only possible !
Some wishes cross'd my mind and dimly cheer'd it,
And one or two poor melancholy pleasures,
Each in the pale unwarming light of hope
Silvering its flimsy wing, flew silent by—
Moths in the moonbeam !—

------

                            —Behind the thin
Grey cloud that cover'd, but not hid, the sky,
The round full moon look'd small.

------

The subtle snow in every passing breeze
Rose curling from the grove like shafts of smoke.

———

     —On the broad mountain top
The neighing wild colt races with the wind
O'er fern and heath-flowers.

———

     —Like a mighty giantess
Seized in sore travail and prodigious birth,
Sick Nature struggled : long and strange her pangs,
Her groans were horrible ;—but O, most fair
The twins she bore, Equality and Peace.*

———

     —Terrible and loud
As the strong voice that from the thunder-cloud
Speaks to the startled midnight.

———

Such fierce vivacity as fires the eye
Of genius fancy-crazed.

———

The mild despairing of a heart resign'd.

———

*For the Hymn on the Sun.*

    —The Sun (for now his orb
'Gan slowly sink)—
Shot half his rays aslant the heath, whose flowers
Purpled the mountain's broad and level top.

———

&ast; This is the substance of the latter part of the second strophe, in the original version, of the *Ode to the Departing Year* (see Vol. i. p. 170, *note*).—ED.

Rich was his bed of clouds, and wide beneath
Expecting Ocean smiled with dimpled face.

———

### For the Hymn on the Moon.

In a cave in the mountains of Cashmeer there is an image of ice, which makes its appearance thus: Two days before the new moon there appears a bubble of ice, which increases in size every day till the fifteenth, by which time it is an ell or more in height;—then as the moon wanes, the image decreases till it vanishes away.

———

In darkness I remain'd;—the neighbouring clock
Told me that now the rising sun at dawn
Shone lovely on my garden.

———

These be staggerers that, made drunk by power,
Forget thirst's eager promise, and presume,
Dark dreamers! that the world forgets it too!

———

     —Perish warmth,
Unfaithful to its seeming!

———

Old age, 'the shape and messenger of death,'
His wither'd fist still knocking at death's door.

———

    —God no distance knows
All of the whole possessing.

———

With skill that never alchemist yet told,
Made drossy lead as ductile as pure gold.

———

Guess at the wound and heal with secret hand.

———

           The broad-breasted rock
Glasses his rugged forehead in the sea.

———

I mix in life, and labour to seem free,
    With common persons pleased and common things,
While every thought and action tends to thee,
    And every impulse from thy influence springs.

———

Grant me a patron, gracious Heaven ! whene'er
My unwash'd follies call for penance drear :
But when more hideous guilt this heart infests
    Instead of fiery coals upon my pate,
    O let a titled patron be my fate ;—
That fierce compendium of Egyptian pests !
Right reverend Dean, right honourable Squire,
Lord, Marquis, Earl, Duke, Prince,—or if aught higher,
However proudly nicknamed, he shall be
Anathema Maránatha to me !

———

His own fair countenance, his kingly forehead,
His tender smiles, love's day-dawn on his lips,
The sense, and spirit, and the light divine,
At the same moment in his steadfast eye
Were Virtue's native crest, th' immortal soul's
Unconscious meek self-heraldry,—to man
Genial, and pleasant to his guardian angel.
He suffer'd nor complain'd ;—though oft with tears
He mourn'd th' oppression of his helpless brethren,—
Yea, with a deeper and yet holier grief
Mourn'd for the oppressor.   In those sabbath hours

His solemn grief, like the slow cloud at sunset,
Was but the veil of purest meditation
Pierced thro' and saturate with the rays of mind.

———

Within these circling hollies, woodbine-clad—
Beneath this small blue roof of vernal sky—
How warm, how still! Though tears should dim mine
    eye,
Yet will my heart for days continue glad,
For here, my love, thou art, and here am I!

———

Each crime that once estranges from the virtues
Doth make the memory of their features daily
More dim and vague, till each coarse counterfeit
Can have the passport to our confidence
Sign'd by ourselves. And fitly are they punish'd
Who prize and seek the honest man but as
A safer lock to guard dishonest treasures.

### A Sober Statement of Human Life, or the True Medium.

A chance may win what by mischance was lost;
   The net that holds not great, takes little fish;
In some things all, in all things none are crost;
   Few all they need, but none have all they wish:
Unmingled joys to no one here befall;
Who least, hath some; who most, hath never all!

═══

### Translation of a Latin Inscription by the Rev. W. L. Bowles *in Nether Stowey Church.*\*

Depart in joy from this world's noise and strife
To the deep quiet of celestial life!

\* *Literary Remains of S.T.C.*, vol. i. p. 50.

Depart!—Affection's self reproves the tear
Which falls, O honour'd Parent! on thy bier;—
Yet Nature will be heard, the heart will swell,
And the voice tremble with a last Farewell!

*Epilogue to The Rash Conjuror,*
*An Uncomposed Poem.*

We ask and urge—(here ends the story!)
   All Christian Papishes to pray
   That this unhappy Conjuror may,
Instead of Hell, be but in Purgatory,—
     For then there's hope;—
     Long live the Pope!*
1805.

*Sentimental.†*

The rose that blushes like the morn
   Bedecks the valleys low;
And so dost thou, sweet infant corn,
   My Angelina's toe.

But on the rose there grows a thorn
   That breeds disastrous woe;
And so dost thou, remorseless corn,
   On Angelina's toe.
1825.

*The Alternative.†*

This way or that, ye Powers above me!
   I of my grief were rid—
Did Enna either really love me,
   Or cease to think she did.
1826.

* *Literary Remains of S.T.C.*, vol. i. p. 52.
† *Ib.* vol. i. p. 59.

*Written on a fly-leaf of a copy of* " Field on the
Church," *folio,* 1628, *under the name of a former
possessor of the volume inscribed thus :*
" *Hannah Scollock, her book, February* 10, 1787."

This, Hannah Scollock! may have been the case;
Your writing therefore I will not erase.
But now this book, once yours, belongs to me,
The Morning Post's and Courier's S.T.C. ;—
Elsewhere in College, knowledge, wit and scholarage
To friends and public known as S. T. Coleridge.
Witness hereto my hand, on Ashly Green,
One thousand, twice four hundred, and fourteen
Year of our Lord—and of the month November
The fifteenth day, if right I do remember.*

*Translation of a Fragment of* Heraclitus.

Μαινομένῳ στόματι ἀμυριστὰ καὶ ἀκαλλώπιστα
φθεγγομένη, &c.

——Not hers
To win the sense by words of rhetoric,
Lip-blossoms breathing perishable sweets ;
But by the power of the informing Word
Roll sounding onward through a thousand years
Her deep prophetic bodements.†

" The angel's like a flea,
   The devil is a bore ;—"
No matter for that! quoth S.T.C.,
   I love him the better therefore.‡

* *Literary Remains of S.T.C.*, vol. iii. pp. 57, 58.

† *Ib.*, vol. iii. p. 419.

‡ *Ib.*, vol. iv. p. 52. Written in a copy of Luther's *Table-talk.*

## EPIGRAMS.

### I.

#### *On a late Marriage between an Old Maid and a French Petit Maître.*

Though Miss ——'s match is a subject of mirth,
  She consider'd the matter full well,
And wisely preferr'd leading one ape on earth
  To perhaps a whole dozen in hell.*

### II.

#### *On an Amorous Doctor.*

From Rufa's eye sly Cupid shot his dart
And left it sticking in Sangrado's heart.
No quiet from that moment has he known,
And peaceful sleep has from his eyelids flown.
And Opium's force, and what is more, alack!
His own orations, cannot bring it back.
In short, unless she pities his afflictions,
Despair will make him take his own prescriptions.*

### III.

Of smart pretty fellows in Bristol are numbers, some
Who so modish are grown, that they think plain sense
    cumbersome;
And lest they should seem to be queer or ridiculous,
They affect to believe neither God or old Nicholas!†

* *The Watchman*, April 2, 1796; *Literary Remains of S.T.C.*, vol. i. pp. 45, 46.

† *The Watchman, ubi suprà* (in the course of a Letter signed S. T. COLERIDGE).

### SONNET

*On receiving a letter informing me of the birth
of a son.**

When they did greet me father, sudden awe
Weigh'd down my spirit : I retired and knelt
Seeking the throne of grace, but inly felt
No heavenly visitation upwards draw
My feeble mind, nor cheering ray impart.
Ah me ! before the Eternal Sire I brought
Th' unquiet silence of confused thought
And hopeless feelings : my o'erwhelmed heart
Trembled, and vacant tears stream'd down my face.
And now once more, O Lord ! to thee I bend,
Lover of souls ! and groan for future grace,
That ere my babe youth's perilous maze have trod,
Thy overshadowing Spirit may descend,
And he be born again, a child of God !

*Sept.* 20, 1796.

### On Deputy ———.†

By many a booby's vengeance bit,
I leave your haunts, ye sons of wit !
And swear by Heaven's blessed light
That Epigrams no more I'll write.
Now hang that * * * * * for an ass
Thus to thrust in his idiot face,
Which, spite of oaths, if e'er I spy,
I write an Epigram—or die !

LABERIUS.

* Enclosed in a letter to Thomas Poole. Printed in the
Biographical Supplement to *Biographia Literaria* (*Vide anteà*,
vol. i. pp. 149-151).

† *Morning Post*, January 2, 1798.

*To a well-known Musical Critic, remarkable
for his ears sticking through his hair.**

O —— ! O —— ! of you we complain
For exposing those ears to the wind and the rain.
Thy face, a huge whitlow just come to a head,
Ill agrees with those ears so raw and so red.

A Musical Critic of old fell a-pouting
When he saw how his asinine honours were sprouting ;
But he hid 'em quite snug, in a full frizz of hair,
And the Barber alone smoked his donkeys rare.

Thy judgment much worse, and thy *perkers* as ample,
O give heed to King Midas, and take his example.
Thus to *publish* your fate is as useless as wrong—
You but prove by your ears what we guess'd from
your tongue.                                   LABERIUS.

## ΕΓΩΕΝΚΑΙΠΑΝ.

[The following burlesque on the Fichtean Egoismus may,
perhaps, be amusing to the few who have studied the system,
and to those who are unacquainted with it, may convey as
tolerable a likeness of Fichte's idealism as can be expected
from an avowed caricature.]

*The Categorical Imperative, or the Annunciation of the
    New Teutonic God, ΕΓΩΕΝΚΑΙΠΑΝ : a dithy-
    rambic Ode, by Querkopf Von Klubstick, Grammarian,
    and Subrector in Gymnasio.* * * * *

*Eu ! Dei vices gerens, ipse Divus,*
(Speak English, friend !) the God Imperativus,
Here on this market-cross aloud I cry :
I, I, I ! I itself I !

---

* *Morning Post*, January 4, 1798.

The form and the substance, the what and the why,
The when and the where, and the low and the high,
The inside and outside, the earth and the sky,
I, you, and he, and he, you and I,
All souls and all bodies are I itself I !
        All I itself I !
        (Fools! a truce with this starting!)
        All my I ! all my I !
He's a heretic dog who but adds Betty Martin!"
  Thus cried the God with high imperial tone :
In robe of stiffest state, that scoff'd at beauty,
A pronoun-verb imperative he shone—
Then substantive and plural-singular grown,
He thus spake on :—" Behold in I alone
(For Ethics boast a syntax of their own)
Or if in ye, yet as I doth depute ye,
In O ! I, you, the vocative of duty !
I of the world's whole Lexicon the root !
Of the whole universe of touch, sound, sight,
The genitive and ablative to boot :
The accusative of wrong, the nominative of right,
And in all cases the case absolute !
Self-construed, I all other moods decline :
Imperative, from nothing we derive us ;
Yet as a super-postulate of mine,
Unconstrued antecedence I assign
To X, Y, Z, the God Infinitivus ! *


*The Briage Street Committee.   An Impromptu.*
        Jack Stripe
        Eats tripe,
        It is therefore credible
        That tripe is edible.

* *Biographia Literaria*, Lond. 1817, vol. i. pp. 148, 149 note.

And therefore perforce
It follows of course
That the Devil will gripe
All who do not eat tripe.

And as Nick is too slow
To fetch 'em below,
And Gifford the attorney
Won't quicken the journey;
The Bridge-Street Committee
That colleague without pity
To imprison and hang
Carlile and his gang,
Is the pride of the city :
And 'tis association
That alone saves the nation
From death and damnation.*

## To Nature.

It may indeed be phantasy when I
Essay to draw from all created things
Deep, heartfelt, inward joy that closely clings ;
And trace in leaves and flowers that round me lie
Lessons of love and earnest piety.
So let it be ; and if the wide world rings
In mock of this belief, [to me] it brings
Nor fear, nor grief, nor vain perplexity.
So will I build my altar in the fields,
And the blue sky my fretted dome shall be,
And the sweet fragrance that the wild flower yields
Shall be the incense I will yield to thee,

* *Letters, Conversations and Recollections of S.T. Coleridge*,
Lond. Moxon, 1836, vol. i. pp. 90, 91.

Thee only God ! and thou shalt not despise
Even me, the priest of this poor sacrifice.*

---

> What boots to tell how o'er his grave
> She wept that would have died to save ;
> Little they know the heart who deem
> Her sorrow but an infant's dream
>    Of transient love begotten ;
> A passing gale that as it blows
> Just shakes the ripe drop from the rose—
>    That dies, and is forgotten.

> Oh woman ! nurse of hopes and fears,
> All lovely in thy spring of years,
>    Thy soul in blameless mirth possessing ;
> Most lovely in affliction's tears,
>    More lovely still those tears suppressing.†

---

> So Mr. Baker heart did pluck—
>    And did a-courting go !
> And Mr. Baker is a buck ;
>    For why ? he *needs* the *doe*.‡

---

### *Lines in a German Student's Album.*

[The Germans, of all mortals the most imaginative, take extraordinary delight in their albums; and Coleridge being a noticeable Englander, and a poet withal, was not unfrequently requested to favour with a scrap of verse persons who had no very particular claims

---

\* *Letters, Conversations and Recollections of S. T. C.*, vol. i. p. 144.

† *Ib.*, vol. ii. p. 75.       ‡ *Ib.*, vol. ii. p. 21.

upon his muse. As a specimen of the playful scintillations of this gifted man upon such occasions, I subjoin the following quatrain, which he wrote when about to leave the University in the *Stammbuch* of a Göttingen student who had the same course of lectures (*Collegium*) with him *] :—

" We both attended the same College,
    Where sheets of paper we did blur many,
And now we're going to sport our knowledge,
    In England I, and you in Germany."

### EPIGRAM ON KEPLER.

*From the German.*

No mortal spirit yet had clomb so high
As Kepler—yet his Country saw him die
For very want ! the *Minds* alone he fed,
And so the *Bodies* left him without bread.†

———

Whene'er the mist that stands 'twixt God and thee
Defecates to a pure transparency
That intercepts no light and adds no stain,—
There Reason is, and then begins her reign !‡

### DISTICH.

*From the Greek.*§

Jack finding gold left a rope on the ground ;
Bill missing his gold used the rope, which he found.

---

* Carlyon's *Early Years and Late Recollections.*

† *The Friend*, p. 231.

‡ *On the Constitution of the Church and State*, by S. T. Coleridge. Lond. 1830, p. 227.

§ *Omniana*, 1812, vol. ii. p. 123.

[The lines " To a Lady offended by a sportive observation that women have no souls " (*vide suprà*,
p. 308), also originally appeared in *Omniana*,
vol. i. p. 238.]

## NOTES.

### NOTE TO VOL. I. P. 29.
#### *The Raven.*

This poem on its original appearance in *The Morn-ing Post*, was preceded by the following mock epistle :—

"Sir,—I am not absolutely certain that the
following Poem was written by Edmund Spenser, and
found by an Angler buried in a fishing-box : —

" ' Under the foot of Mole, that mountain hoar,
Mid the green alders, by the Mulla's shore ' ;

" but a learned Antiquarian of my acquaintance has
given it as his opinion that it resembles Spenser's
minor Poems as nearly as Vortigern and Rowena the
Tragedies of William Shakespeare.—This Poem must
be read in recitative, in the same manner as the
*Ægloga Secunda* of the *Shepherd's Calendar*.

"CUDDY."

### NOTE TO VOL. I. PP. 129-132.
#### *Introduction to the Sonnets.*

This Introduction originally appeared as the Preface to a privately-printed pamphlet of sixteen pages
(1796), containing a selection of twenty-eight Sonnets
from various Authors, made "for the purpose of bind-
ing them up with the Sonnets of the Rev. W. L.

Bowles." The concluding paragraph, which afterwards gave way to that printed in the text, ran as
follows in the pamphlet :

"Miss Seward, who has perhaps succeeded the best
in these laborious trifles, and who most dogmatically
insists on what she calls the sonnet-claim, has written
a very ingenious although unintentional burlesque
on her own system, in the following lines prefixed to
the Poems of a Mr. Carey." (And then the lines are
quoted.)

The selection that follows contains three Sonnets
of Bowles, "not in any edition," notes Coleridge
in MS., "since the first quarto pamphlet of his
Sonnets"; four of Southey; four of Charles Lloyd;
two of Charlotte Smith; one specimen each of Thomas
Warton, Bamfylde, Henry Brooke (the author of *The
Fool of Quality*), Sotheby, Thomas Russell, Thomas
Dermody, and Anna Seward; and last, but not least,
four of Charles Lamb, and four of Coleridge's own,
which it will be worth while to particularize. Of those
of Lamb two had appeared as Effusions XI. and XIII.
in the first edition of Coleridge's Poems : the other
two were those beginning—

"We were two pretty babes, the youngest she,"
and

"When last I roved these winding wood-walks
    green,"

both of which afterwards appeared, together with
others, in the second edition of 1797. But in the
pamphlet Coleridge has appended the following
printed editorial footnote to the line in the former
Sonnet—

"And hid in deepest shades her awful head !"

"Innocence, which while we possess it, is playful as

a babe, becomes AWFUL when it has departed from us. This is the sentiment of the line—a fine sentiment and nobly expressed.—EDITOR."

The four Sonnets of his own which Coleridge has included in this little Selection are as follows :—

> *To the River Otter.*
> *On a discovery made too late.*
> *"Sweet Mercy! how my very heart has bled."*
> *To the Author of the Robbers.*

In the last-named Sonnet, as it appears in the pamphlet, Coleridge took occasion to remove a 'bull' which had been pointed out to him in his first edition, where he wishes to *die*—

> " Lest in some after moment aught more mean
>    Might stamp me mortal !"

In doing this he transposed the four opening lines, and altered the word " mortal " to " human," thus :—

> " That fearful voice, a famish'd father's cry,
>    From the dark dungeon of the tower time-rent,
>    It thro' the shuddering midnight I had sent,
>    Schiller ! that hour I would have wish'd to die—
>    That in no after moment aught less vast
>    Might stamp me human ! " &c.

In the second edition, while the other alterations are adopted, the opening lines are redistributed into their original places, and the word " human " is altered back to " mortal."

At the end of this Sonnet, in a copy of the pamphlet now lying before me, Coleridge has written :—" I affirm, John Thelwall ! that the six last lines of this Sonnet to Schiller are strong and fiery; and you are

the only one who think otherwise.—There's a *spurt*
of author-like vanity for you !"

The copy in question of this singularly interesting
pamphlet is bound up, according to Coleridge's intention, at the end of a copy of the fourth edition of
Bowles's *Sonnets and other Poems*, published at Bath
in 1796, throughout which not Coleridge certainly and
presumably Thelwall, who is apostrophized, as we
have seen, in one of the MS. notes, and to whose wife
this copy was given, has written in the margins a
number of sarcastic and disparaging remarks on poor
Mr. Bowles's verses, which constitute a wholesome
antidote to the strong dose of hyperbolical and extravagant laudation administered by Coleridge, who has
written the following presentation note in a fly-leaf of
the same copy :—

"DEAR MRS. THELWALL,

"I entreat your acceptance of this volume,
which has given me more pleasure, and done my heart
more good, than all the other books I ever read, ex-
cepting my Bible. Whether you approve or condemn
my poetical taste, the book will at least serve to re-
mind you of your unseen, yet not the less sincere
friend,        "SAMUEL TAYLOR COLERIDGE.

"Sunday Morning,

"December the eighteenth, 1796."

There is nothing in history or literature to match this,
unless it be the infatuated passion of Queen Titania
for Bottom in the *Midsummer Night's Dream*. This
volume is now in the Dyce Collection at the South Kensington Museum. At the end of it is inserted a printed
slip containing the lines "To a friend who had declared
his intention of writing no more poetry," signed S. T.
COLERIDGE. This is apparently the form in which

they appeared in a Bristol newspaper in 1796. They
offer no variation of text; but the word "nostril"
in the antepenultimate line is marked in ink, presumably by Coleridge himself, with a plural "s."

### NOTE TO VOL. I. P. 131.

*" to write pathetic Axes, or pour forth extempore Eggs
and Altars !"*

The ancient little wits wrote many poems in the
shape of Eggs, Altars, and Axes.

(MS. Note by S. T. C. in the volume described
above.)

### NOTE TO VOL. I. P. 148.

(No. iv. of the *Miscellaneous Sonnets.*)

This Sonnet is much improved in the third edition;
but I cannot recollect the alterations. There were
three or four Sonnets, of which so many lines were
written by Southey, and so many by me, that we
agreed to divide them, in order to avoid the ridiculous
anxiety of attributing different lines in the same short
poem to two different authors.

(MS. Note by S. T. C., in a copy of the edition of
1797, now in the possession of Mr. Frederick
Locker.)

### NOTE TO VOL. I. P. 176.

*Ode to the Departing Year,* Epode ii. *" Hence for
many a fearless age."*

" Hence thro' many a fearless age
   Has social Freedom loved the land,
Nor alien despot's jealous rage
   Or warp'd thy growth or stamp'd the servile brand."

(Thus quoted in Coleridge's treatise *On the Constitution
of the Church and State,* Lond. 1830, p. 18).

## NOTE TO VOL. II. P. 238.

### *The Three Graves.*

The original manuscript copy from which *The Friend* (in which this poem first appeared) was printed, bound in a folio volume, is one of the many priceless treasures bequeathed by the late Mr. John Forster to the South Kensington Museum. The prose introduction to *The Three Graves* is in Coleridge's own writing : the poem itself, like Mr. Payne Collier's Salisbury MS. of *Christabel*, is in the writing of Miss Sarah Stoddart, with interlineations and corrections in Coleridge's hand. " I have not," he writes at the head of the poem, " voluntarily been guilty of any desecration of holy names." The variations, beyond those already indicated in the foot-notes, are for the most part un-important and trifling. The penultimate stanza of the fourth part originally opened thus :—

> " He sat upright; and with quick voice
> While his eyes seem'd to start; "

but this is scored through, and the reading in the text (see p. 254) substituted in Coleridge's hand. In the Introduction we have silently corrected, on the au-thority of this manuscript, two or three corruptions of the text, attributable to the Penrith printer who ori-ginally set up the type of *The Friend*.

## NOTE TO VOL. II. P. 282.

### *Fragment of a Poem entitled " The Wanderings of Cain."*

Quoted in Coleridge's *Aids to Reflection*, Lond. 1825, p. 383, as " the first stanza of the poem, composed in the same year in which I wrote the *Ancient Mariner* and the first book of *Christabel*" [i.e. 1797].

" Chance or his happy genius leads the poor be-nighted pilgrim to an oasis or natural garden, such as in the creations of my youthful fancy I supposed Enos the child of Cain to have found."

### Note to Vol. ii. p. 283.

*" Hyman Hurwitz, Master of the Hebrew Academy, Highgate."*

" Let a friendly antagonist retort on *my* scheme of faith in the like manner : I shall respect him all the more for his consistency as a reasoner, and not confide the less in his kindness towards me as his neighbour and fellow-Christian. This latter and most endearing name I scarcely know how to withhold even from my friend Hyman Hurwitz, as often as I read what every reverer of Holy Writ and of the English Bible ought to read, his admirable *Vindiciæ Hebraicæ!* It has trembled on the verge, as it were, of my lips every time I have conversed with that pious, learned, strong-minded, and single-hearted Jew, an Israelite indeed and without guile."

Coleridge's *Aids to Reflection*, Lond. 1825, p. 205, note.

### END OF VOL. II.

ROBERT ROBERTS, PRINTER, BOSTON.